GW00659927

A Pharmacist's Tale

A Pharmacist's Tale

— ❖ —

John Newstead

JOHN NICKALLS PUBLICATIONS

This is a narrative of the joys, delights, disappointments and problems I encountered whilst collecting and preserving, for future generations, some of this country's 'pharmacy history'. The project was finally completed in 1985 after twenty-five years research. It can now be found in the Bridewell Museum, Norwich, where it is displayed as a complete pharmacy of years gone by.

Dedicated to Janie, my aide memoire – and Ian, my aide electronique.

John Newstead
Taverham

First published 2003
© John Newstead 2003

All rights reserved. No part of this publication may be reproduced, in any form or by any means, without the prior consent of the author.

ISBN 1 904136 10 9

Published by John Nickalls Publications,
Oak Farm Bungalow, Sawyers Lane, Suton, Wymondham,
Norfolk NR18 9SH

Designed by Ashley Gray and printed by Geo R Reeve Ltd,
9–11 Town Green, Wymondham, Norfolk
NR18 0BD

Contents

— ❖ —

CURTIS AND CO.'S
IMPROVED INHALER.

Exhibited at the

of London,

MANUFACTURED
ON
PRINCIPLES

RETAIL PRICE,

Medical Society

Monday, Nov. 4, 1867.

APPROVED
BY
DR. QUAIN, ETC.

7s. 6d.

THE GENERAL CHARACTERISTICS OF THIS INHALER ARE—
Simplicity of Arrangement, Cleanliness, Strength, Portability, Extended Surface for Evaporation, Free Ingress of Air, which must pass through the material of inhalation.

The *Lancet* writes, dated Jan. 11, 1868 :—" This Inhaler possesses the advantage of being much more portable than any that are at present in use. It is of extremely dwarf shape, and provided with an elastic air-tube, so that the patient can conveniently use it when in a reclining position, as the instrument may rest on the pillow without danger of upsetting. This apparatus is also well adapted for the administration of Chloroform, Ether, Creasote, and other volatile substances, as, from its construction, the exact quantity required may be inhaled. Having these advantages, and being sold at the low price of 7s. 6d., there can be no doubt but that it will be extensively employed."

The *Medical Times* writes, dated January 18, 1868 :—" During the present epidemic of scarlet fever, a good Inhaler is of the greatest possible service to practitioner and patient. The Inhaler before us possesses the merit of cleanliness and portability, and of being easily used by a patient in bed without the risk of being upset."

Important Notice.—Reduction in Price.
CURTIS & CO.'S SYRUP OF THE SUPERPHOSPHATE
OF IRON, QUININE, AND STRYCHNINE,

Has been pronounced by the highest Medical Authority to possess tonic powers far exceeding all other preparations. It is always uniform in character, and has never been known to produce any unpleasant symptoms, due to its careful mode of preparation. This Syrup has been prescribed, both at home and abroad, for more than ten years. 5s. 4d. per lb.

Proprietors of PASMA, or HEALING POWDER, and
PLASMA, or PASMA cum GLYCERINÂ.
ORIGINATED BY
CURTIS & CO., PHARMACEUTISTS,
48, BAKER STREET, LONDON, W.

Advertising material, dating from the 1860s, for an inhaler for the administration of chloroform, ether, creosote and other volatile substances.

Introduction

— ❖ —

WHEN I came back to Norwich in 1960 to start my own business I found the chemist shops that I knew in my youth were all being modernised or closed and I felt that I ought to do something to save a little of their past; this is an account of a collection started in 1960 to its present permanent position in the Bridewell Museum in Norwich, where it has been since 1985. It entailed many journeys all over East Anglia to chemist shops that had closed, or were about to close, for various reasons, such as re-location, retirement, refurbishment or bereavement.

The chemist shops visited were in cities, towns and villages all over East Anglia; from Lincolnshire in the north, down to Cambridgeshire, across to Norfolk and Suffolk, and down into Essex, each one having its own unique character. Most of them had cellars and attics and many had living accommodation either behind or above the shop. Electricity was

Row & Taylor Ltd, Chemists, St Stephen's Street, Norwich, about 1950. The shop stands next to Marks & Spencer, whose department store is on the same site today.

7

G Shreeve MPS, Chemists, Westcliff-on-Sea, taken in the 1920s. The picture shows the living accommodation above the shop.

On the opposite page; a list of personalities from the 'Chemist & Druggist' of 1875.

usually connected only to ground and first-floor rooms, and access to cellars and attics required the use of strategically placed candles.

Heating was usually very sparse, especially in the smaller shops. Where gas was connected a small heater was placed behind the shop counter and another in the dispensary where there was also a gas tap on the counter, which was used to melt the sealing wax when wrapping medicines, and also to connect to a Bunsen Burner when heat was needed for certain preparations. There was no heating in storerooms, cellars or attics and re-stocking shelves was a coat and gloves job in winter. Products such as Olive Oil and Castor Oil had to be stored in the living quarters to prevent cloudiness and solidification occurring in the wintertime.

My first encounter with the pharmacies was usually on my half-day after finding out that the business was about to close, or had already done so. This meant closing my shop promptly at 1pm on a Wednesday, having a quick bite to eat and venturing into the unknown. Was it going to be an Aladdin's Cave, or a completely wasted journey? All will be revealed in the following chapters.

From four counties in East Anglia I returned from my forays with multiple items (ie. a car or van load) from thirty-eight different pharmacies – and from another fifty or more just a few items in a cardboard box was all I got for my troubles. Some visits were a waste of time altogether, there being nothing left worth salvaging, but I felt that I had to find out for myself just how these businesses had disappeared. One Norwich pharmacy with 200 years of documented history closed and the premises were cleared in 1980 with just a few recent labels surviving. Outside East Anglia, changes in pharmacy were also happening at the same rate, but I had to resist the temptation to extend my borders, otherwise I could never have coped with it all.

From the 'Chemist & Druggist' journal of 1875.

Personalities.

MR. C. PARKER has succeeded to the business of Mr. Haythornthwaite at Kirkby Lonsdale.

MR. JAMES TILSON has succeeded Mr. J. N. Sutterby at Long Sutton.

MR. HEY, chemist, Bridge Street, York, was seriously injured by the accidental discharge of his companion's gun while shooting on "the first." It is feared that he will lose the sight of both eyes.

MR. HALTON, druggist, of Earlestowne, Lancs., was thrown from a trap which came into collision with a tramcar at Haydock on September 1. He was seriously injured.

THE business of Mr. J. Walker, of 24 Cropley Street, New North Road, N., has been sold to Mr. Hartshorn, through the agency of Messrs. Tench & Taylor, of 38 Walbrook, E.C.

MR. MANFIELD's business at 129 Oldfield Road, Salford, Manchester, has been sold to Mr. F. D. Scholes, through the agency of Messrs. Tench & Taylor, of 38 Walbrook, E.C.

MR. ADAM'S business at Winchester has been disposed of to Messrs. E. B. & T. W. Bolton (late of Ipswich), through the agency of Messrs. Tench & Taylor, of 38 Walbrook, E.C.

THE business of Mr. Charles Gold, at Shepherd's Bush, has been disposed of to Mr. John Edmunds (late of Battersea Rise), through the agency of Messrs. Tench & Taylor, 38 Walbrook, E.C.

Chapter One

Pharmacies and Pharmacists

— ❖ —

U NLIKE today, many pharmacies were owned and run by the Proprietor Pharmacist on his own, the premises having changed very little from the previous owners before that, and in some cases the fixtures and fittings were original from when the shop opened, as far back as 1700, or earlier.

The shop counters, shelves, and cabinets were all mahogany and glass, and everything was out of reach of the public until the 1950s when new shops appeared with light wood fittings and open plan layouts. Refitting of the old shops began – and that's where I came in.

Before the National Health Act came into being in 1948 the pharmacists ran their business, as had their fathers and grandfathers before them, closely guarding the secrets of their own medicinal

Gardiner & Lacey, Dispensing Chemists, Norwich were situated at the Guildhall Pharmacy, No. 3, St Giles' Street.

On the left, a picture of F S Cullen of No 5, Barrack Street, Norwich, taken around 1900, seen here in collar, tie and morning jacket, as mostly worn in those days. However, there were exceptions as the picture on the right shows of J H Corbyn of Stradbroke, Suffolk.

preparations, carefully recording all prescriptions in their Prescription Book. They mostly wore collar, tie and morning jacket or white coat, but there were exceptions.

All medicines were wrapped in white paper, tied with dispensing twine, and sealed with sealing wax before handing out to the customer. In my early days in pharmacy, where I was taught how to fold and crease the paper wrapping on a bottle, it used to make me cringe when a customer would rip off the packaging and look at the label to make sure it was the right medicine before pocketing the bottle and handing back to me the crumpled wrapping. By the time I heard of the pharmacies closing the pharmacists had mostly reached the stage where they had endured enough pharmacy in their lives, living and working on the same premises through the war years and then coming up to their retirement age, having to cope with the changes of the National Health Service. As there was no goodwill value on the pharmacies that were closing, every item, however old or unsaleable, had a value and each of my visits involved haggling at some point.

Not all of my journeys were successful. On one occasion, on one of our mutual half-days, I arranged to meet an elderly pharmacist at his shop. After waiting outside in the rain for over an hour after the agreed meeting time it did not please me when he said he had fallen asleep after

The inside view of a typical pharmacy, taken in 1920 by time exposure.

his lunch, however, on unlocking and entering the shop, I thought it was all worth while. The fittings of curved mahogany and glass with gold lettering were really impressive, as were the rows of blue and green bottles, pink and blue ointment pots, and swan-necked carboys on the shelves behind the counters. Through the dispensary and past the bench cluttered with scales, pill machines, pestles and mortars, and other assorted dispensing equipment (*see colour plate on page 25*), we carefully descended the steep stone steps into the cellar to behold a virtual treasure trove of even older pots, jars and bottles. At this stage I could contain myself no longer. "How much of this can I buy from you", I said. His swift reply was: "Oh, there's nothing here for sale, young man. All this will go when I sell the business, I just thought you would like to see it". Completely deflated I mumbled a quick 'thank you' before setting off on a dismal, depressing ride home in the rain. I never did discover what happened to it all, I didn't even get a label, and I understand that the pharmacist died shortly afterwards before selling the business. I consoled myself with the fact that I could never have afforded it anyway!

In complete contrast, I received a letter from an elderly pharmacist in Essex who was closing down his shop due to ill health and had been advised by an Inspector of The Royal Pharmaceutical Society of Great Britain that I could probably help in disposing of the contents of his shop.

My wife and I were invited to his house for Sunday lunch on a cold

February day and we soon found out that both him and I had competed in a full-bore rifle meeting a few years earlier. The conversation never got round to the reason for our visit until after lunch when the pharmacist suggested that we followed his car – a powder-blue MGB-GT – to the shop. The journey was quite exciting, trying to keep up with a sports car through the deserted streets of a seaside town on a wintry Sunday afternoon, but we managed to keep up, probably because there were no other cars about that day and no police to check on our speeding.

When we stepped inside the shop door it was like going back in time. It was freezing cold and dimly lit, and although there were up-to-date items (ie 1975) on the counters, all the bottles and jars on the shelves were as they had been since the pharmacist's father had owned the shop from 1906. The gloomy atmosphere created by the dull unpolished mahogany fittings and grey ceiling (the pharmacist smoked a pipe), was only slightly improved by sunlight shining through the stained glass window backs and coloured liquids of the large carboys in the windows, but I felt that here was something that needed to be preserved.

After a brief tour of the shop, the pharmacist asked me to price it all, which I started to do, but soon discovered after counting just the bottles on the shelves that I had already passed the figure that I could afford. In the meantime I was informed that I could not pick and choose items, I

G Shreeve & Son, shop interior taken in 1920.

would have to buy everything, so I continued to write down figures which, by now, had ceased to mean anything as there was no way I was going to buy it all.

Moving from the shop into the dispensary the same routine applied, noting down all the items, but by now with little enthusiasm. Two more storerooms received the same treatment and then came the crunch! "Right then, how much for the lot?"

With fingers crossed I said I could afford only my original amount. Expecting to be shown the door I was amazed when he grabbed my hand and said: "Done, now I want it all cleared out within the next ten days, or I shall have to charge you rent", which he did for one week until I was able to go back and collect it all. The dismantling, transporting and storage of everything is a story in itself (*Chapter Nine*) but the fittings formed the basis of my collection and can now be seen in the Bridewell Museum in Norwich.

I was fortunate to know Guy Robinson, a fellow pharmacist in Norwich who qualified in 1936 and had researched his family's pharmacy in Dereham, Norfolk from 1820 up to 1963. I have two audio tapes of him talking about pharmacy in his father's day, which we put

The Author's shop at Sprowston, Norwich, taken in 1960.

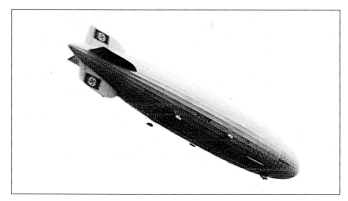

A Nazi Zeppelin seen somewhere over the coast of Essex in the 1930s.

together some years ago and the details of his life are fascinating. He related an event that took place in September 1916 when a German Zeppelin airship bombed Dereham with considerable destruction to property and some loss of life. The pharmacy windows were shattered and a fire caused by incendiary bombs falling on the ironmonger's warehouse necessitated evacuation of the house connected to the pharmacy. His parents, who had at that time five children from infancy to ten-years-old, were joined by soldiers billeted in the town to carry them in their night clothes to a safer residence.

As a Chemistry Laboratory Monitor at school in 1947-1948, I experimented with chemicals and caused a few upsetting moments for the school staff. One of these was when I was evaporating an obnoxious mixture in a fume-cupboard which was not properly sealed. The heavier-than-air fumes leaked out and down the outside wall into the classroom beneath, which had to be evacuated, and I had to terminate the experiment promptly. On another occasion I produced an explosive compound as a crystalline solution; when dropped on the tiled floor of the school corridors the solution dried out and when walked upon small explosions were caused, similar to those created by toy gun percussion caps. The headmaster was not amused.

I then decided to 'work from home' and tried to find a sympathetic pharmacist from whom I could buy chemicals. I soon learned that the word 'Poison' was interpreted in different ways by different pharmacists, some of whom did not take kindly to being told by a 17-year-old what was on, or off, the Poisons List. In hindsight, I think they did not want to spend time weighing out small amounts of powders and liquids costing pennies to a schoolboy. However, one pharmacist was very helpful, always asking how I was progressing with my experiments (I would add that, by this time, I had got over producing stinks and bangs and was on to more complex processes such as trying to identify plant constituents).

Mr. James Watson,

FAMILY & DISPENSING CHEMIST,

Rose Corner, Norwich.

SCIENCE and Invention have been very active in devising means to alleviate human suffering, both by Medicinal Remedies and Mechanical Appliances For those who take an interest in the subject a visit to Mr. James Watson's Establishment is full of instruction. Here we find surgical and other appliances for almost every form of weakness or defect. Trusses and Bandages for Weak Knees and Ankles, Ladies' Abdominal Belts, Riding Belts for Gentlemen, Silk and Cotton Elastic Stockings for Varicose Veins, &c., besides appliances for the Nursery, Sickroom, or Hospital, such as Bed Pans, Urinals, Air and Water Beds, Pillows and Cushions, Enema Apparatus, Waterproof Sheeting, &c. Among the most conspicuous of these specialities, Trusses and Abdominal Belts rank prominently. The new Serotal Truss is a valuable appliance in severe cases, and altogether the stock of Trusses here is supposed to be the largest and best assortment in the Eastern Counties. The " Perfection " Abdominal Belt, of which Mr. Watson keeps a large stock, is of new design, and claims to be superior to any other yet introduced. Among other specialities in this branch are the Proplastic Spinal Support, and Chest Expanding Braces and Guards for Cricketers. The shop is a handsome business-like Establishment in a prominent corner position at the junction of Rose Lane and King Street. It is facing the back of the Agricultural Hall and General Post Office, and close to the Cattle Market, the Thorpe Terminus being only a few minutes distant. The interior is well fitted up, and a large stock of proprietary articles is kept, patent medicines, medicinal preparations, lotions, pills, and other preparations, besides pure drugs and chemicals of every description. Among the noted preparations are some specialities compounded by Mr. Watson, which have gained a wide popularity. Among these are " J. Watson's Cough Pills," for Coughs, Asthma, and Bronchial Affections; "Watson's Quinine and Bark Pills," and " Watson's Powders and Ointments," for the piles. One of the most valuable of the specialities in this department is the noted Foot Powders prepared by Mr. Watson and applied to tender feet to prevent swelling or chafing. It is largely patronized by pedestrians and athletes with the best results. In mixtures, condiments, draughts, and powders, for horses and cattle, Mr. Watson also does a large business ; and, as the shop is close to the Cattle Market, it is a centre of great activity on each succeeding market day, farmers and others availing themselves of their visit to town to lay in supplies. The dispensing branch receives special attention, being under Mr. Watson's direct personal supervision, and all physicians' prescriptions and family recipes are promptly and accurately compounded of the purest drugs. The business is an important one, with a sound connection among the leading families in and around Norwich, farmers, clergymen, and others. Mr. Watson is a Chemist of great experience, and has the confidence and respect of all classes.

Jarrold and Sons, Printers, Norwich, Yarmouth, and London.

Sometimes my request was for obscure chemicals, but the pharmacist would ask around and usually came up with what was required. The point of all this is that, on my return to Norwich as a qualified pharmacist in 1960, I met up again with that same pharmacist and on his retirement I was able to purchase his dispensing scales, which had been used for my benefit years before and they now occupy the centre space on the dispensing bench of the collection.

A group of photographic wallets from the '20s and '30s.

As in most walks of life, pharmacy had its share of outstanding 'characters' and East Anglia was no exception. I have already briefly mentioned Guy Robinson's early life in Dereham, but there was a well-known pharmacist, Mr James Watson, whose shop was at Rose Corner, King Street, Norwich, that I would like to have met. He registered as a pharmacist in October 1890, and I vaguely remember the shop in the 1940s as the place where my eldest sister bought a special cough mixture for my father. A friend who helped me on several occasions (*see Chapter Three*) was related to Mr Watson through marriage, and he set about researching the history of the family and the pharmacy. He has gathered together a lot of information, which I hope can be incorporated into the history of Norwich chemists sometime in the future. The illustration on the opposite page shows a copy of a hand-out leaflet advertising Mr Watson's wide range of medicines and sundries.

Pharmacies in seaside resorts had a good seasonal trade in photographic material, the sale of films, albums and other accessories, but the most lucrative was the developing and printing of customer's films. Not everyone collected their holiday snaps, but all were kept in a box in a drawer, season after season, in case the owners returned on holiday and asked for them. Some of these holiday mementoes went back many years and I remember a lady coming into my first retail pharmacy in Folkestone asking for her photographs from three years earlier. They

Two photographs, dating back to the 'thirties, which remained uncollected from a pharmacy.

were apparently the last ones on which her late husband appeared and it was very gratifying to be able to hand them over to her and see her obvious joy as she looked through the prints. Sometimes it was not quite so simple, a mix up by the processing firm could result in the wrong prints in the wrong wallets, such as a prize bull instead of sandcastles and deckchairs, and this could cause considerable disruption with customer relationships.

Quite often photographic chemicals were packed and sold by pharmacies, many labels being found in several locations. A chance opening of a door at the back of one pharmacy, that had been closed for quite some time, revealed a small photographic studio and darkroom with everything still in its place, from the large wood and brass portrait camera on its stand, smaller plate cameras and antiquated flash equipment, to the more mundane earthenware trays and vats for processing and printing films. As this was not strictly pharmaceutical I contacted a local TV photographic expert who removed and purchased everything from the proprietor to prevent it from being destroyed.

In the coastal towns of East Anglia there was an additional trade from foreign ships and sailors, whose purchases in the eighteenth and nineteenth centuries of medical supplies were paid for with foreign gold coins, which were weighed against brass disks (*see colour plate on page 25*) with values stamped on them in sterling (pounds & shillings) according to the weight of gold. I was not aware of their existence until I found three such items in a box with other mixed weights in a back room of a pharmacy that had been closed for a long time and had been emptied and stripped of its fittings and stock. These very dirty discs revealed their details on cleaning and were confirmed by the British Museum as representing the weight and value of Portuguese Pieces and Moidores.

I often found things which had no apparent pharmaceutical connection, for instance, in a back storeroom of a shop there was a First World War French bayonet standing in a corner on its own. In the room next door, which had originally been living quarters, was a small ornate cast-iron fireplace and grate and, having a second look at the blackened end of the bayonet, I realised that it had been used long ago as a poker.

Not so easy to work out was the small cardboard box left in a drawer of a pharmacy that had been closed for some time. Underneath tissue paper in the box were a number of very small bottles, corked and sealed with brown wax, each containing a dried brown spider, without any label on the bottles. As this was the same place where I found the brass weights for weighing foreign gold, I wondered if these arachnids had any connection with foreign sailors, but I could not get anywhere with identification as the spiders were too mummified. I still look at these in the cabinet at the Bridewell Museum and wonder if they were intended for medical use, or something obscure that I could not even imagine.

Although most chemist shops were similar in appearance and layout their trade was often quite different. In some small country towns and villages there was a healthy trade in veterinary and agricultural supplies, many of which were sold under the name of the pharmacy although prepared by a manufacturing chemist, which catered for domestic pets, farm animals and agrochemicals, eg tonic and cleansing drinks for cattle, warble-fly powder, pig powder, horse balls, seed-dressings and diarrhoea powders for dogs (see colour plate on page 26).

These were often the things which had been packed away in storerooms as their use diminished to give way to more modern products. Thank goodness many of these were bulky items and difficult to dispose of easily, otherwise they would certainly not have survived.

Pharmacists/Opticians were not uncommon in the past, incorporating their optical work in the pharmacy, from dispensing prescriptions to retiring into a backroom or upstairs to carry out an eye-test or fit spectacles. My first of only two employers was such a person, a large man with a loud voice, who would put his head round the corner of the dispensary and say: "Newstead, hold the fort, I have a consultation!", as he stomped upstairs to his 'cubbyhole' as it was known to his staff. In some pharmacies a separate room for eye-tests was no bigger than a cupboard with space for a shop chair and a sight-test chart on the wall, privacy being maintained by a thick velvet curtain drawn across the entrance. Many other pharmacist/opticians had larger facilities, quite often separated from the actual pharmacy (*see colour plate on page 26*).

Many pharmacies were capable of carrying out simple chemical analyses on substances brought into the shop by customers, eg urine analysis for diabetics, but some pharmacists with a keen interest in chemistry had small laboratories equipped for more complicated work. Some of the more obscure chemicals were often encountered, although I had no idea what they could have been used for. One small laboratory that I found was crammed full of glass equipment; flasks, beakers, retorts, burettes, distillation apparatus and rows of small analytical reagent bottles – a chemistry student's dream. Unfortunately, it was a case of 'look, but don't touch' as it had all been promised to the pharmacist's grandson. The packing and transportation of all that fragile glass would have been a nightmare, I told myself, and I didn't have anywhere to display it.

Although I tried to keep my activities within East Anglia, I did accept an invitation from a small manufacturing chemist in Hertfordshire, which was relocating and had some old apparatus for disposal. With my wife navigating the car, we followed the given instructions along country lanes until we came to large wrought-iron gates with a small brass plate indicating that we had arrived. Along a tree-lined drive we came up to an impressive country mansion, wondering where the factory was going to be. Greeted at the door by one of the directors, we were shown into a large hall with marble floor and pillars leading to a wide staircase. Ushered into a small sideroom office we were offered tea or coffee and had explained to us that the house was just the head office of the company and all the firm's activities had been transferred to a new up-to-date building on an industrial estate. After our coffee we were taken through the house to the rear of the building where there was a single-storey flat-roofed laboratory attached. This was where the firm manufactured their products, which were largely prepared from animal sources.

The apparatus was certainly antiquated, but much too large for me to consider having in my collection, although we did take some of the smaller items such as a copper hot-air oven, used for drying monkey glands, which we gave to a friend for incubating pheasant eggs, and a copper water bath which I believe became a plant pot holder! Even though there was nothing to enhance our collection we learned a lot about this specialised pharmaceutical manufacture on a small scale and I can still recall the pungent sickly smell of that laboratory.

Chapter Two

Dustbins
and Sheds

— ❖ —

A VISIT to a small village pharmacy in Suffolk did not look very promising as I arrived on one of my precious half-days. Through the small glass panes of the window and doors I could see that the shop was bare. Empty wooden shelves and stained walls showed the shapes and outlines of bottles that had been there for years – but where were they now? The pharmacist had died some time previously and his wife had cleared the shop. When I asked about the bottles and jars she said that they were the last to go, in fact they were still out at the back of the shop. With my pulse increasing I followed her down the passage to an outside brick-paved yard, and there stood four galvanised dustbins. With a flourish the elderly lady whisked off two of the dustbin lids and exclaimed: "What about that then?" All four bins were full to the top with smashed glass-stoppered bottles in shards of green, blue, brown and clear glass, with odd pieces of ointment pots and a couple of large pear-drop carboy stoppers. Trying to mask my disappointment, I told her that I would have given her at least £200 for those bottles and, with a sigh and lowering of her shoulders, she suggested that I might like to look in the outside toilet, which was full of cardboard boxes – mostly empty. Sorting through the boxes I came across several brown paper bags full of corks in various sizes, also a couple of bone spatulas, a small paper package of gold leaf and several old display adverts, all of which I bought (*see colour plate on page 27*).

Nearby in the yard, an old rusty incinerator showed where all the labels and other papers were disposed of, sadly leaving nothing for me to trace the history of this tiny pharmacy, but at least I did not leave empty-handed on this occasion. Before I left I was invited into the back parlour for a cup of tea and shown a beautiful, small wooden, Victorian medicine chest and a collection of watercolours painted by one of my ancestors, John Ninham. But sadly, they were of too sentimental value and I could not even think of asking the lady to part with them. Later on I was able to learn more about this small pharmacy from the records of The Royal Pharmaceutical Society of Great Britain.

Another 'bin' episode happened on a visit to a small town in the Cambridgeshire Fens where a pharmacist had just taken over an old family business and was happy for me to look at the old 'junk' he wished to get rid of. He had not got round to throwing anything away so the old labels were still there, as were many other small original items. A quick look outside the back door revealed the dustbin. No broken bottles! However, by the side of the bin was a cardboard box tied up with twine, waiting to be collected with the other rubbish later that day. A brief glance inside was all I needed to realise that here was something really special. Inside the cardboard box was a collection of sixty-four small blue handmade cardboard boxes with lids. About the size of a matchbox, each containing a small amount of a different substance, mostly of vegetable origin such as seeds, fruits, leaves, barks, resins, insects and many other items used in pharmacy and medicine. On the inside of each lid was a description of the contents giving the name of the item in Latin, the country of origin, its constituents and uses. This was part of an apprentice's Materia Medica (*see colour plate on page 27*), used for identification purposes in preparation for taking the Chemist & Druggist practical examination, and must have been used in the 1920-1930 period. This really was a rare find which is now safely in the collection at the Bridewell Museum Norwich.

From past experience, I soon found out that many of the best 'finds' were in the most unlikely places, tucked away and forgotten, originally put on one side in case they were ever needed again. Pharmacists were reluctant to throw things away and, as there were no sell-by dates, things just seemed to accumulate, which was fortunate for me.

One such case was in Cambridge where a small pharmacy had been refitted several years previously. Much of the original fittings and contents had already disappeared, but behind the shop was an old open-sided bicycle shed containing a tarpaulin-covered heap consisting of a broken weather-worn set of mahogany drawers (*see colour plate on page 28*), with some original glass knobs, and although most of the drawers had collapsed, some of the mahogany fronts were retrievable. There were also piles of collapsed cardboard boxes which had burst open and scattered their contents of old empty glass medicine bottles over another pile of glass-stoppered bottles with coloured-glass labels, many of which were still in a reasonable condition, although it was quite a task matching the ground-glass stoppers to the individual bottles.

I had a telephone call in 1975, from a pharmacist who had taken over a village pharmacy a year previously and had sorted out a large box of old stock that he thought I might be interested in. Arranging to visit this small shop on my half-day I had the feeling that it was not going to be a good day for me as I stepped down into the crowded shop of three people and waited, and waited. Eventually the pharmacist poked his head round the door of the dispensary and, knowing that I was not one of his customers, invited me into the back of the shop directing me to the back yard where the inevitable sheds were located. The first shed was an outside toilet with a blue and white floral design Royal Doulton toilet, with a polished-oak seat and cover, hemmed in by double packs of coloured toilet-rolls. The second much larger shed contained just about every household thing that had been replaced over the years. In the back of the shed were old iron bed-frames, metal window-frames, a long-handled ten-inch lawnmower, a wooden roller mangle and, hanging on the wall, an assortment of rusty, broken garden tools, including a scythe and a fiddle seed-drill.

In front of all these items, and just inside the door, stood a large tea-chest covered with an old blue velvet tablecloth and a paper label saying: "To be collected by Mr Newton". As this was close to being my name, I assumed that this was meant for me. A quick glance inside confirmed this. The tea-chest was too bulky and heavy for me to lift on my own and so, as the pharmacist was still busy with his customers, I had to drag the loaded tea-chest across the unpaved muddy yard to the side gate by which I had parked my estate car.

With an elderly neighbour's help the now rather dirty package was manhandled into the back of the car. By that time I was hot, exhausted and dying for a cup of tea, but a quick look inside the shop, to say goodbye to the pharmacist, showed that there was no chance of a drink as the shop was still full of customers (not the same three, surely?). Arriving home, I off-loaded the tea-chest (cleaning the mud from the car would have to wait) and had my cup of tea before examining my gift. It was certainly a box of mixed items, starting with a top layer of old cosmetics with faded labels through being in a window display too long. The packs of face powder were from the 1950s, some of which had split and distributed their contents over the items beneath, which consisted of old propriety preparations, pills, toothpowders, cough and indigestion mixtures, ointments, suppositories etc, all of which were resting on a layer of old surgical dressings, some of which were interesting and retrievable, such as red-flannel bandages, cyanide dressings and a few things that I had never seen before. There were **Claxtons Ear Caps** for babies – fine frilly lace caps with small square pads and pink bows to cover the ears and pink satin tape to fasten under the chin – to flatten protruding ears. **Zudor Jackets** (*see colour plate on page 28*), chest and lung protectors in two sizes, children and adult (cotton padded garments) and **Capsicum Chest Warmers** (cotton wool impregnated with capsicum, a rubefacient). My wife's grandfather wore one all winter through to May! Another unusual dressing was a **Crepe Binder** in a cardboard box, which depicted a woman in, what I can only describe as, a body tube, elasticated and made from 50% wool – it was claimed to give invaluable support after all abdominal operations.

Underneath the layer of dressings was a horrible brown smelly sticky mess composed of jars of Calf's Foot Jelly (also known as Cow Heel Jelly), several of which were broken. Fortunately the bottom layer in the tea-chest was made up of split packs of cotton wool dressings and sanitary towels, which had soaked up some of the messy part of which had probably provided sustenance to the family of mice that had made a home in the bottom of the tea-chest. Calf's Foot Jelly was originally prepared in the home, as the 1927 recipe below illustrates.

CALF'S FOOT or COW HEEL JELLY

2 calf's feet or 1 cow heel	6 oz. sugar
2 quarts water	Whites of 2 eggs
$\frac{3}{4}$ pint lemon juice and white wine mixed	Shells of 2 eggs (crushed)
Rind of 3 lemons	

Method: Divide the feet into pieces; wash them in warm water, removing all marrow and fat. Put them into a saucepan, cover with cold water and bring to the boil. Throw away this water, add 2 quarts of cold water, cover, and simmer gently for 5–6 hours. The liquid should be reduced to a little less than 1 quart. Strain and leave until quite cold.

Carefully remove all fat and place the jelly in a large saucepan with the rest of the ingredients. Clear as for Aspic Jelly (*see above*).

Turn into a mould and leave to set. This jelly is often prescribed for invalids.

Note: The jelly should set satisfactorily alone, but $\frac{1}{4}-\frac{1}{2}$ oz. gelatine may be soaked in the lemon juice and wine if the jelly from the cow heel does not appear to be sufficiently stiff to set again when diluted with the lemon juice and wine.

On a long shelf in an outside storeroom of a village pharmacy I came across a large number of rusty 1lb lever-top tins that looked like paint pots. On closer examination these turned out to be waterglass – a thick, viscous, clear liquid of sodium silicate used for preserving new-laid hens eggs, each tin having a large label with directions for preserving eggs as seen on page 29 (from Pharmaceutical Formulas, Vol II, 1934).

Above: The dispensary bench cluttered with scales, pill machines, pestles and mortars.

Below: Discovered in the back room of a pharmacy were this set of weights originating from the eighteenth and nineteenth centuries.

A selection of veterinary products, many of which were sold under the name of the pharmacy, although prepared by a manufacturing chemist.

Not uncommon in the past, some pharmacists incorporated optical work from their premises, even those unable to read were catered for!

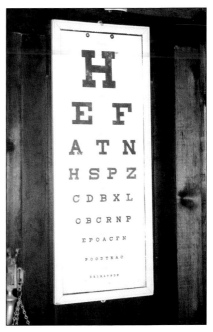

Above: Sorting through some boxes were several brown paper bags full of corks of varying sizes and a couple of bone spatulas – as well as a packet of gold leaf!

Below: An apprentice's Materia Medica collection, used for identification purposes.

A broken, weather-worn, set of mahogany drawer fronts, some with the original glass knobs.

Norvic Binder, a body tube claimed to give support after all abdominal operations; Claxtons Ear Caps to flatten protruding ears; Zudor Jackets chest and lung protectors for adults and children.

SOLUTION OF WATERGLASS

the most efficient and inexpensive medium

For Preserving Eggs

DIRECTIONS

Remove the lid from the tin by levering it up with a penny. Select a wooden, earthenware, or galvanised iron vessel of the capacity of about a gallon and a half, and empty into it the contents of this tin. To the waterglass in the vessel add 7½ pints of hot water, and mix well together by means of a wooden or other suitable stirrer. Let the solution become quite cold, then place the eggs, which should be perfectly fresh, in the liquid. The above quantity of solution will be sufficient for from 120 to 150 eggs, but care must be taken that about an inch of liquid is left above the eggs.

The vessel containing the eggs and solution is next lightly covered to exclude dust, and stored in a cellar or other cool place. If some of the liquid in the preserving-vessel evaporates on keeping, restore it up to the proper level by adding water.

Eggs so preserved will keep for twelve months, and are ready for use as soon as taken out of the solution, the egg merely requiring rinsing with warm water or wiping with a damp cloth. If the eggs are to be boiled, they should be pricked in two or three places before placing in the saucepan to prevent the eggs cracking.

The process is only intended for preserving fresh eggs. If the eggs have been laid some time before placing in the waterglass, the results are not satisfactory.

The solution is quite harmless to the hands or clothes, and possesses antiseptic or preservative properties. A fresh solution is required for each season's supply, as the liquid becomes exhausted in time.

Waterglass, or Isinglass, was used to preserve new-laid eggs, with each tin coming with directions for its use.

I remember well, the white enamel bucket covered with muslin, on the cold floor of the pantry at home and seeing my mother on her knees lifting the cover and carefully placing new-laid eggs in the bucket.

A coal shed at the back of a pharmacy was not the ideal place to search, but one small brick-building proved to be different. The originally white-washed walls were black with coal dust and cobwebs; torn damp, smelly, cardboard boxes had been thrown in on top of each other and in the back of the shed were dozens of earthenware bottles, which I first thought were Ginger Beer bottles or similar. Clambering over the pile of dirty boxes to reach the heap of mostly broken bottles, and getting absolutely filthy in the process, I found that the heap consisted of several sizes of brown earthenware jars with wax-sealed bungs, a few of which had enough remnants of paper labels to identify the contents. There were two different products, a **Solution of India Rubber** and **Harness Liquid** (*see colour plate on page 45*), for beautifying and preserving, without labour, Coach and Gig harness, etc, etc, price 6d and 1/. The labels also bore the wording 'By Appointment to His Highness Prince Albert'.

In some of the older pharmacy properties I found large quantities of sawdust, in barrels or tea-chests, and I had to ask what it was for. Obvious to the older pharmacist, but not to me! In shops where the only electricity was for lighting, the shop floor had to be sprinkled with damp sawdust and swept up with a brush as there were no vacuum cleaners.

Chapter Three

Cellars, Attics and Lofts

— ❖ —

CELLARS were the places that I dreaded most. What nasties would I find lurking under layers of dust in the dim and pungent atmosphere, which was after all the safest place for potent and dangerous preparations of which there were several, such as concentrated acids, liquid ammonia, caustic alkalis, arsenic, strychnine and cyanides, to name but a few. If the cellar had electric lights and good wooden stairs I was much happier, it indicated that it had been used regularly, but if it was stone steps and candlelight I knew I had to be cautious. In one such cellar, quite similar to the wine cellars of Burgundy with grey and blue moulds on the walls and roof, were many bottles whose labels I could not read from a distance of about one metre, and I had no intention of getting any closer as there was a large orange slimy fungus creeping down one wall and across the floor, convincing me there was nothing on those shelves that interested me.

Another cellar with an arched brick roof had no shelves, but bottles and jars were scattered all over the floor, some of which were worth saving, but mostly unlabelled and uninteresting. The brick floor of the cellar sloped down away from the steps, the side walls getting narrower and the ceiling lower, until it was impossible to stand upright , at which point it had been bricked up. It was, in fact, a tunnel under the road, originally going down to the river next to the house where Cardinal Wolsey was born in Ipswich.

A similar, but much larger cellar, was found in Wisbech which was in a much better condition and had also originally extended under the road and down to the river. Although having been blocked off just under the road the traffic noise and vibration was considerable and I did not spend long in that part of the cellar.

Many cellars were small and empty except for wooden and cardboard boxes, old empty medicine bottles and other discarded items, but in one such cellar in a Norwich pharmacy, dating from 1790, I found a pile of pieces of mahogany, obviously a fitting of some sort, so it was brought home and put together by a carpenter friend to restore it to its original form as a mortar stand. This was invaluable in making ointments in the wintertime when there was no, or very little, heating in the dispensary. Inside the stand was a metal container with wire handles into which was poured hot water. An earthenware mortar was then placed on the top of the stand and warmed thoroughly before adding and mixing the ointment bases, which would have been quite hard at the ambient dispensary temperature. The active ingredients were then easily incorporated into the ointment (*see colour plate on page 45*).

A dark brown bottle, of an unknown substance standing alone on a corner shelf in a cellar, caught my eye where it was above a row of several glass bottles of apparent opaque glass. On close inspection the cracked container proved to be made from Gutta-Percha, a coagulated latex derived from Palaquim trees, which grow in Malaysia and Sumatra. The contents of the bottle, which had leaked onto the shelf below and etched the surface of the glass bottles, had been Hydrofluoric Acid, a colourless fuming liquid which attacks glass very strongly. Nowadays, strong plastic is used to contain this obnoxious chemical.

Attics and lofts were the source of most of the old pharmaceutical items that I was able to rescue as, unlike cellars, deterioration through dampness was not such a problem. Many pharmacies were built with accommodation included and originally the pharmacist would live over the shop with his wife and family. Gradually, this practice ceased, although my first shop in 1960 was built this way and the living quarters

Antiquated telephone extensions enabled the Surgeon to communicate with his Dispenser in an adjoining room, or issue instructions to his Coachman!

Left: This ancient telephone extension was discovered in one of three, first-floor stockrooms.

Below: Also discovered were tins of labels from previous past-generations of pharmacists dating back to the nineteenth century.

became stockrooms with the attic used as the place to put things that were used less frequently, eg Christmas packaging and advertising materials. The rooms with their small coal-grate fireplaces and coloured floral wallpaper had tea-chests stacked on their sides against the walls, or some kind of makeshift shelving. There was usually a built-in cupboard or two in the larger room, which would have been the family living-room. One such property I came across was in Cromer, Norfolk, where the shop had been re-arranged several times over the years, but structurally the building was as originally built, with two storeys above the shop and an extended dispensary at the rear, in what was a former fisherman's cottage. On the first floor were three large full stockrooms, with an antiquated telephone extension, above which was an unused attic.

Inside this room, with its steeply tiled roof, was a shambles. Coming in through a broken window, pigeons had been roosting there for many years on a table of unknown age – unknown, due to an all-over covering layer of pigeon excrement. On the wall opposite the door was a fireplace and chimney breast with floor to ceiling wooden cupboards on each side. On one side the cupboard shelves were full of tins containing labels, from previous generations of pharmacists, dating back to the nineteenth century, which have proved very helpful in tracing the pharmacy's history and the other cupboard was even more of a 'treasure-trove'. The shelves were crammed full of boxes, bags, tins and jars of old drugs, originating from all over the world, which were used in medicine and kept in the pharmacy in the drawers of the 'Drug Runs'. Most of these drugs were in an excellent condition and have now been relocated in the relevant drawers in the Bridewell Museum, where they help to create the smell associated with old chemist shops.

A loft of a black wooden barn-like warehouse, at the back of a Fenland town pharmacy, was also a source of some unusual items. The pharmacist had taken over an old family business and invited me to sort through the warehouse. The shop had been altered some time before and had nothing of any great age, but the warehouse seemed promising. The ground floor was full of large empty cardboard boxes, advertising material, drums of lime-wash powder and an old trade bicycle. A wide open-tread wooden staircase gave access to the first floor where the ancient floorboards had gaps between them giving a good view of everything on the ground floor. When walked upon, the boards creaked, and on every step there was a rattling sound like rain on a corrugated-iron roof. On investigating it was discovered that the noise was coming from some barrels at one end of the room, which were in a dilapidated state, releasing their contents of mustard seed through the gaps in the floorboards on to the trade-bike below.

In the centre of this well-ventilated room stood a large wooden bench with deep drawers in which were two green jugs – copper covered in verdigris – and alongside the bench there were several boxes, most of which appeared to be empty. One large box full of wood-wool seemed interesting, it contained an original full display for **Yardley Old English Lavender** complete with its Dresden porcelain figure and dummy packs of perfume and toilet water, none of which had ever been unwrapped. This complete unit was given to The Royal Pharmaceutical Society of Great Britain and was on display at the London headquarters in Bloomsbury Square, but at the moment it is in store off the premises with the rest of the Society's collection (*see colour plate on page 46*).

Many other attics were explored and found to be empty, some were not investigated where the property was old and neglected, as on one visit my feet went through a stairway leading to a third floor, which persuaded me not to proceed any further. I shall never know if I missed some treasure!

The quantity of some of the substances found amazed me at times, such as a large heavy mahogany chest giving out a beautiful spicy aroma, which was found to be full of Cloves, thousands of them, while another barrel was full of Linseed. Did the apprentice drag them up the stairs, or were they filled up from smaller containers? I suspect the former was more likely.

In small town and county pharmacies, part of their business was in supplying farmers with agricultural chemicals often in bulk – for use as weedkillers, sheep-dips, pesticides and killing rats and mice – and these were usually stored in the cellars, which was just as well as many of these were extremely dangerous. I was always wary of finding these chemicals when sorting through the gloomy, cluttered, neglected areas of cellars and looked out for any containers with extra warning labels on them. There were some very nasty things I discovered that I wished I had not – boxes of bottles containing Nicotine (for use against pests in greenhouses), bottles of Bromine liquid (how ever did I dispose of them and what were they used for?) and countless jars of Potassium Cyanide for destroying wasps' nests, accompanied by the odd bottle or two of Phosphorus, White Arsenic and assorted Caustic Alkalis and concentrated acids.

In one of these cellars a friend, who was helping me, showed me a brown glass bottle and asked if it was dangerous. When I saw that it was Hydrocyanic Acid I told him to put the bottle down very carefully and go and wash his hands immediately, as the poison is rapidly absorbed by the skin. I was winding him up really, it was not that serious, but all the way home he kept asking what the symptoms of poisoning were, and what could he do about it? His reaction stayed with me for many years, he really thought he was going to die in that cellar! That little brown bottle was actually used for putting down stray dogs and cats. In the same cellar was an assortment of screw-cap jam-jars with a thin solid layer in the bottom. I did not open them as I remembered from my youth being told that a chemist could supply 'killing bottles' for butterflies and moths to collectors. The jars contained a layer of Plaster of Paris impregnated with a small quantity of Potassium Cyanide, sufficient to stupefy insects without affecting human beings.

In another of the dark, damp cellars I found a dust-covered clear glass jar, corked and sealed with wax, full of clear liquid, which contained off-white sticks about the size of cigarette sweets. Although the label had disintegrated, I recognised the sticks as white phosphorus, stored under water. Checking that the wax seal was intact, I packed the bottle in a box of wood-wool and transported it back to my home very carefully.

As phosphorus ignites on exposure to air I didn't think it wise to retain it in case of accidents, so I had to devise a way of getting rid of it safely. At that time the local council had no means of disposing of such chemicals.

On a sunny windless day, I cut off a small piece of one of the relatively soft sticks and placed it in my vegetable garden between two rows of potatoes. It gradually changed colour to yellow, then red, through to deep purple, at which stage a thin wisp of white smoke arose into the air like a piece of string, continuing until there was nothing left but a small white patch on the surface of the soil. As there was no flame ignition I continued using the same amount on each suitable day on a different part of the garden for several weeks until all the phosphorus had gone. I had to cordon off the vegetable patch with wire netting, while dealing with this problem, to keep our rottweiler away, as she was fascinated by this strange phenomena. A few weeks later we had a bumper crop of potatoes!

In some of the very old pharmacies the poison cupboard, being quite large, was located in the cellar and contained poisons for many uses, including those used in medicines such as Strychnine, which was also used for killing moles, but as the Poison Laws were gradually updated, and the use of these older substances diminished, a more secure Poisons' cupboard became obligatory in all pharmacies for the storage of controlled drugs and poisons. Strychnine was commonly used in small doses in tonics. In one pharmacy a man presented a prescription for large doses of Tincture of Nux Vornica (which contains Strychnine). The pharmacist pointed out that the dose was excessive and would be fatal, to which the man replied: "That int fer me, tha's fer my old bull".

Similarly, Arsenic Solution was used widely, as related by Leslie Matthews, our leading Pharmaceutical Historian who served his apprenticeship with F S Cullen in Norwich. One of his jobs was making up tonics containing another poison, Tincture of Aconite, with three drops in one fluid ounce of water supplied to canary fanciers to help the canaries sing. These birds were kept by the 'Outwork Weavers' of the textile industry, who occupied the upper floors of houses in Norwich, and in a way were the forerunners of radios.

Chapter Four

Fixtures and Fittings

— ❖ —

THE furniture, fixtures and fittings in all pharmacies before modernisation were similar, each one having wall shelf-units, counters, sets of drawers, dispensing screens or benches, baby scales and chairs for customers' use. The overall use of mahogany gave a sombre atmosphere, which was not enhanced by the usually dim lighting.

Each shop was fitted out individually with the wooden fittings permanently positioned so that the layout of the pharmacy was the same for most of its life, or the life of the pharmacist at least, and remained looking good with its polished wood, brass handles, sparkling cut-glass knobs on drawers and ornate light fittings, that is until I started to dismantle everything. The mahogany sets of drawers (drug-runs) were often the most disappointing units, the front of the drawer in fine mahogany was not matched by the rest of the drawer, which was constructed from softer wood and often fell apart on removal of the whole unit from the wall, mostly because of woodworm or dry rot. These units were mostly left to be burned, as I didn't see any point in recovering them. One such drug-run in a small Fenland town had been moved from the front shop and fixed to a wall in a back room where it was falling to pieces, riddled with woodworm. I could see that it had been fitted across a shallow recess in the wall, and on removal a small group of old bottles were revealed, black with dust, and covered with cobwebs. Treasure at last I thought, but a quick wipe with a duster revealed the bottles to be from about 1900. Sadly, only one had a label that had not disintegrated and this was a square green bottle that had contained **Doctor Gregory's Stomach Powder** (*see colour plate on page 46*), presumably put there before the drug-run was fitted.

The drawers themselves contained nothing but rubber bands, paper clips, old razor-blades and two broken clay pipes. As each pharmacy was similarly fitted out and everything had to be removed I accumulated several of each item of furniture and fitting and had to dispose of all but the best which were saved for the collection.

A Norwich pharmacy that was relocated in the 1950s, and again in the 1960s, used much of the original fittings from the first premises (dating from 1854), and on closing down in 1970 these pieces were disposed of. Fortunately, I was able to obtain the large drug-run and another item that I could not find space for in my future collection. This was a 7-foot long examination couch, with a dark brown, polished leatherette covered hard bed, stuffed with horse hair, on a sturdy wooden frame with thick turned wooden legs, which had been used over many years for a variety of uses, such as fitting trusses and other surgical appliances. It seemed a shame to destroy it, so I had a table top lid made to fit completely over the couch, preserving it in its original form, and as such it still remains in use as a table in my cool, dry, wine cellar.

Counters were difficult to remove as they were units of anything up to 14-foot long with a 3-foot wide bench top, glass-doored cupboards along the front and rows of deep drawers behind. Fortunately they could be broken down into separate units but the ancient rusted screws that held them together were a problem. Often the Dispensing bench had a gas fitting and a lead sink attached which required a certain amount of brute

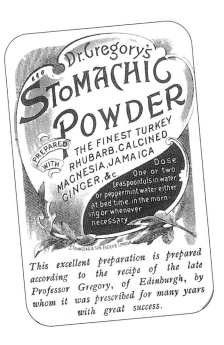

Prepared from the finest Turkey Rhubarb, Magnesia and Jamaican Ginger, according to Dr Gregory's recipe, and prescribed by him for many years.

Advertisements 7

⇢❊ **Established 1826.** ❊⇠

PHILIP JOSEPHS & SON,

Shop Fitters & Show Case Manufacturers,

54, 68, 93 OLD STREET, LONDON, E.C.

ONE of our "Spécialités." Very handsome solid Mahogany "Dispensing Screen," with Counter and Sponge Case, as photo.

PRICE COMPLETE:—

6 ft. long, £13 10s.   7 ft. long, £15 10s.

We keep an immense variety of Fittings, Show Cases, Drug Drawers, Counters, Bottles, Ung. Jars, &c., &c., at bottom prices, and we fit up complete from £50 to £1,000.

TELEGRAPHIC ADDRESS—"JOSIPHIAH LONDON."

An advertisement from 'Diseases & Remedies' of 1898, showing a magnificent, solid mahogany dispensing screen, as supplied by Philip Josephs and Son, of London – one of their specialities!

force to remove from the bench (*see colour plate on page 46*), as did a granite mortar that I found built into a unit in a back room of a chemist's shop. This was supported by a thick wooden platform which had to be removed to get to the mortar, the weight of which was not realised until it crashed through the floorboards. Manhandled and levered across the shop floor, leaving deep grooves all the way to the front door, it took three of us with the aid of planks of wood borrowed from a builder working close by to get it into the van. This massive chunk of rock never reached the final resting-place of the collection – the logistics of transport to the Bridewell museum and negotiating the staircase to the first floor was beyond my means and capabilities. It was left behind when we moved house, having been used for several years as a rather large flowerpot. We never did discover what it was originally used for. The long lignum vitae pestle that accompanied the granite mortar still hangs in the hall of my house and is a constant reminder of its massive partner.

All the pharmacies visited had at least one counter with a label drawer, usually long and shallow with wooden dividers (*see colour plate on page 47*), providing compartments just big enough for the majority of the shop labels and as there were large quantities of assorted labels from all over the region I preserved several of these drawers to house a representative collection.

Most of the labels, all of which were gummed and needed to be moistened (or licked!) before use, were printed with the chemist's name

A small selection of labels to be found in the labels drawer.

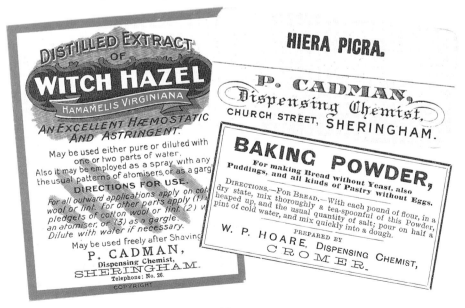

and address and the name of the item to be sold. The range of these labels was enormous, from everyday items such as Castor Oil, Cough Mixtures, Witch-hazel, Brilliantine, etc, to more unusual items such as Steel Wine, Baking Powder, Sewing Machine Oil, Hiera Picra, etc.

As these labels were obtained from a printer, usually in packs of 1,000, the reserves were kept in storerooms, and the quantities found when the shops closed, were extremely large and it was such a shame having to discard the majority of them. At one stage I had four large wine-boxes full, waiting to be sorted out.

As well as label drawers, most counters had a cash-drawer as well, partitioned to take the different denominations of coins with a large section at the back for bank notes, large enough to take the old white £5 note. Apart from a sliding catch and bell underneath which operated on opening the till, the drawer when closed appeared to be no different from any other drawer.

Some pharmacies were more sophisticated and had a wooden till screwed to the counter-top with a paper till-roll to enable sales to be recorded. This type of till was quite common in the 1930s, but the huge metal cash-registers with their large push-buttons, bells and visual display discs – like the National Cash Register tills which started to appear in 1911 and from then on – were in most large stores, and never ever greeted me on my journeys. I would have loved to have had one of those machines to play with and I often feel tempted to try out the one just inside the door of the Bridewell Museum.

Still with counters. After having dismantled several of them I noticed notches along the top back edges which appeared to be consistently regular and it was not until I found a counter with a brass strip along the edge, calibrated in inches and measuring one yard, that I realised what the other marks were. They were for measuring rubber sheeting needed for home confinements, etc, which was cut from a large roll, similar to the system in shops selling cloth and curtain material.

Though seldom encountered today, **Turkey Sponges** (harvested from the sea off the coast of Greece and Turkey – not from a cake-shop) formed an important part of the toilet and baby trade of pharmacies, being used for skin cleansing and bathing, with shop fittings of the 1920s and '30s often incorporating a glass-fronted display unit with gold lettering on the glass. I was fortunate enough to find an empty free-standing glass-fronted mahogany bin for Turkey Sponges (*see colour plate on page 47*), but had quite a shock with the price I had to pay when I bought enough large sponges to effect a display which included a quantity of genuine Aegian sand. Standing on top of the Sponge Bin in the collection we have the

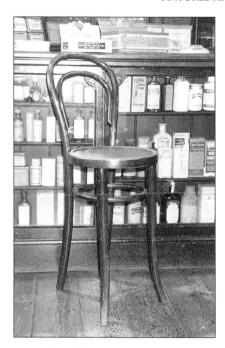 

Most chairs found were of the typical bent cane type, anything unusual with carved shaped backs and turned legs were usually sold to antique dealers following the closure of the shop.

baby-scales. These were my original scales from my first shop, which were regularly used for weighing my customers' offsprings, before this was taken over by the Baby Clinic at the local doctors' surgery.

Chairs provided for customer use only were of different types depending on the quality and location of the pharmacy. The really good ones with carved shaped backs and turned legs did not often survive the shop closure, they were either taken home by the pharmacist or sold to an antique dealer. The more common type of stained, bent cane chair, produced in Czechoslovakia, remained as these were not desirable items of home furniture and they were not comfortable to sit on, at least not for more than a few minutes. One chair I found in a back room of a pharmacy intrigued me – it was a large, wide-seated, wooden chair with thick arms, a high back and a metal ratchet, which once held an adjustable head rest. It was a dentist's chair which had been used by the proprietor's father, also a pharmacist, who pulled out teeth in the 1920s, the fact supported by the discovery in a cupboard of a large tin full of extracted teeth of all shapes and sizes. The chair was subsequently given to the grandson of the pharmacist, from whom I purchased everything when the grandson came to see me several years later, after the death of his grandfather.

To digress a little, I was told a tale by a pharmacist whose father also pulled teeth. Two young brothers went into the pharmacy one morning to have a tooth removed from the seven-year-old, while the eleven-year-old paid his sixpence and watched. In the process of extraction the young patient yelped with pain, his older brother punched the pharmacist in the face, grabbed the sixpence from the bench, took his brother's hand and they both fled from the shop, hiding in a garden shed nearby where they stayed until dusk, fearful of being caught by a policeman. How times change!

Wall clocks were quite common in pharmacies in the 1920–1930 era and were often built into the fittings (*see colour plate on page 47*), although a large number of clocks with advertising on them were supplied free by manufacturers to promote their products and these were hung high up on the wall above the fittings.

Unfortunately, by the time I arrived on the scene, the only evidence of their existence was a round patch of unfaded paint on the wall and screw holes were they had been hung. I was often told that the clocks and antique chairs had been saved for the pharmacist's relatives, but on more than one occasion I suspected that the antique dealer who had taken the old drug jars and pestles and mortars had also persuaded the proprietor to part with these items. The pear-shaped, clear-glass containers of coloured liquid, usually displayed in chemist shop-windows, known as carboys (*see colour plate on page 48*), have since the eighteenth century been a sign of pharmacies and come in two main types with a long 'swan' neck or short stumpy neck and in various sizes. The most sought after were the swan-neck variety with their elegant cut-glass apicular stoppers, but seldom did I have the opportunity to obtain any of these, apart from one occasion where there were three of these large beauties, more than a metre high, that the pharmacist had received an offer for from an American. I persuaded him to accept a slightly higher offer in cash, but as I did not have room in my car for them at the time, I removed the glass stoppers which I took with me as an insurance against being 'gazumped', returning at a later date to collect the carboys. Sadly, one of these three did not survive the final move to the Bridewell Museum, but the other two stand proudly in the collection reflecting light from all angles.

Specie Jars were another eye-catching feature of pharmacies from the end of the eighteenth century (*see colour plate on page 48*), the word 'Specie' being applied to a variety of substances used in pharmacy, the jars being used for storing bulky materials. Some of these large containers

Another group of labels including make up for ladies' legs from the war years.

were of plain glass but, as certain contents were subject to deterioration on exposure to sunlight, the interior of the glass was painted, and by the mid-1800s opaque glass, painted and enamelled on the inside with richly coloured designs of coats of arms and names of contents, was being produced – the finest with domed gold-painted lids. Whilst being eye-catching displays in shop windows and on shelves, not many survived being moved and dusted over the ages, so I was more than surprised when a fellow pharmacist told me there were two large bottles in the loft of his pharmacy and even more surprised and delighted as I stood on the bottom rung of the ladder as he handed down to me two gold-coloured glass-domed lids. Surprise turned to amazement as the two glass jars were gently squeezed through the small trapdoor, followed by a very dusty, coughing pharmacist. Even more amazing, although not in pristine condition, they both survived several journeys to reach their final resting-place intact. Throughout all my 'search and rescue', over more than twenty years, I never came across another Specie Jar.

Chapter Five

Tools of the Trade

— ❖ —

C HEMIST shops were distinct in their layout in that the general public saw only the area in front of the counters. Behind the counters, dispensing screen or in the back room was an unknown world where entry was strictly forbidden and where a piece of paper entered and medicine appeared neatly wrapped in white paper. This miracle required the special needs of tools found nowhere else and which were found in every dispensary.

The most common, and most used items, were the scales (*see colour plate on page 48*) and measures and these I found everywhere.

Glass dispensing measures came in many sizes, from tiny minim measures through a range of increasing volume for dispensing purposes,

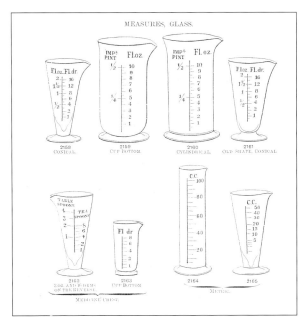

Ranging from tiny minim measures, through to the larger volumes for dispensing purposes, up to one- and two-pint size for measuring bulk liquids.

Harness Liquid for 'beautifying and preserving without labour Coach and Gig Harness'.

It also had the Royal Seal of Approval from His Highness, Prince Albert!

Acquired from the cellar of a Norwich pharmacy, dating from 1790, was this fine mahogany mortar stand, discovered in 'kit form'!

An interesting box of wood-wool revealed an original display for Yardley Old English Lavender, complete with this fine Dresden figurine.

Above: A green bottle of Doctor Gregory's Stomach Powder.

Right: A dispensing bench complete with a lead sink attached, which proved extremely difficult to remove!

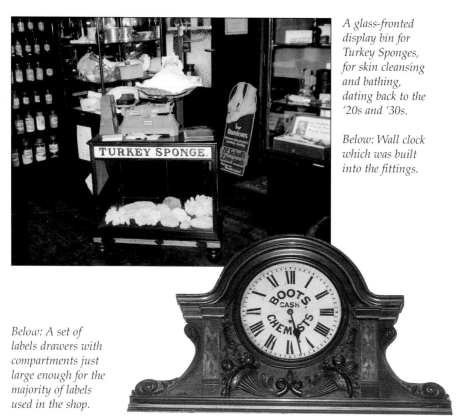

A glass-fronted display bin for Turkey Sponges, for skin cleansing and bathing, dating back to the '20s and '30s.

Below: Wall clock which was built into the fittings.

Below: A set of labels drawers with compartments just large enough for the majority of labels used in the shop.

Above, left: pear-shaped glass containers of coloured liquids, known as Carboys, graced many a chemist's window. Above, right: Specie Jars were another eye-catching feature of pharmacies.

Left and below: The most common and most used items were the scales and these were found everywhere.

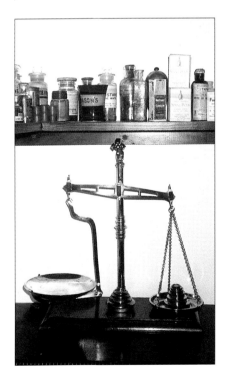

up to larger measures for bulk liquids, eg one pint and two pint size (used exclusively in my own shop for measuring Methylated Spirits). Other glass measures, common to pharmacies, were Medicine Glasses, which were sold over the counter and were calibrated in teaspoons, tablespoons and fluid ounces, usually with a capacity of four tablespoons. Quite often the glasses were also etched with the name of the pharmacy.

The range and shapes of these glass measures was vast, all were officially etched and stamped for dispensing purposes, being calibrated in minims, drachms and fluid ounces, and only occasionally did I find a metric measure, unlike today where everything is metric. All powder and solid ingredients used in medicine had to be measured accurately for dispensing, hence every pharmacy had dispensing scales, which were sensitive in weighing from a few grains up to two ounces.

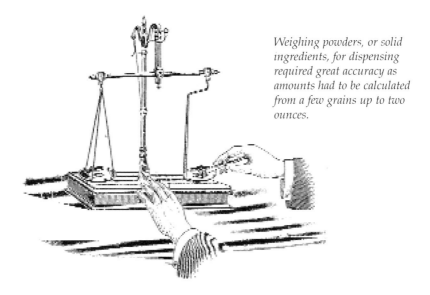

Weighing powders, or solid ingredients, for dispensing required great accuracy as amounts had to be calculated from a few grains up to two ounces.

Larger quantities were weighed on brass shop-scales, varying in size, usually 2lb or 4lb. More often than not all the scales had gone before I arrived on the premises and I was left with a large assortment of weights, from boxes full of small grain weights, right through the range to the largest sizes used for weighing babies. Periodically all weights were checked by a Weights and Measures' inspector and those found to be inaccurate were stamped with a metal punch and should have been rejected, although I did find several groups of such weights in boxes tucked away in drawers. Why they were kept I cannot imagine. Complete sets of weights in fitted wooden boxes (*see colour plate on page 65*) were

DRACHM WEIGHTS. In Sets, 2, 1, ½ drachm, 2, 1, ½ scruple.

In Brass, Stamped		..per set	2/9
,, Unstamped ..		,,	7d.
,, Single Weights, Stamped ..		each	7d.
In Aluminium, Stamped		..per set	4/-
,, Unstamped ..		,,	2/-
,, Single Weights, Stamped ..		each	9d.
In Stainless Steel, Stamped ..		..per set	5/3

GRAIN WEIGHTS. In Sets, 6, 5, 4, 3, 2, 1, ½ grain.

In Brass, Stamped		..per set	2/6
,, Unstamped ..		,,	3d.
,, Single Weights, Stamped ..		each	7d.
In Aluminium, Stamped		..per set	2/9
,, Unstamped ..		,,	4d.
,, Single Weights, Stamped ..		,,	7d.
In Aluminium "Figure," Stamped ..		,,	4/-
,, ,, Unstamped		,,	1/3
,, ,, Single Weights, Stamped		each	9d.
In Stainless Steel, Stamped ..		..per set	4/6

A selection of weights for dispensing.

often found, these were usually metric (grammes) intended for use with a glass-cased chemical balance, of which I only ever found one.

Shapes of weights did not appear to be standard and although the smaller ones were usually of flat, round or square brass, the larger ones were also made of iron. There were some very interesting shapes in the smaller brass weights, triangular, oval and shield, several sets of weights made from aluminium also turned up, which I took to be from the 1939–1945 period when brass was scarce.

From the dispensary bench drawers of most of the pharmacies I collected sticks of sealing wax, thick, thin, short and long, which were essential for use when anything from the dispensary had to be wrapped in white paper and sealed, the paper also being found in ream upon ream, in many sizes. As this was before Sellotape, the other essential item in any pharmacy was the string box – a turned, lidded, boxwood container with a ball of string inside, which usually sat upon the shop counter (*see colour plate on page 65*). Fine dispensing twine was kept on the dispensing bench or in a drawer.

Pestles and mortars were traditionally associated with pharmacy and the older ones of brass and bronze were highly sought after by collectors for their attractive decorative appearance and historical interest, but very seldom did I ever manage to obtain any of these, except on one occasion when I offered a pharmacist more than he expected for his fittings and bottles. A casual enquiry as to whether, or not, he had any older items produced a selection of bronze mortars (*see colour plate on page 66*) from a back room, which had been put away for an antique dealer to look at. He was however quite happy to accept my offer for them.

Iron pestles and mortars, usually rusty, were also encountered in small numbers, but worth cleaning and preserving. Small glass sets were not uncommon, but usually chipped or incomplete with the pestle missing. Those made of earthenware were everywhere as they were still in use in the pharmacies and I finished up with a large number of these in all sizes, so many that friends and family at the time were persuaded to make room for a set in their kitchens.

As mentioned previously, empty glass medicine bottles had accumulated everywhere I went, especially when the changeover from imperial (fluid ounces) to metric occurred, and I had to be ruthless and leave them to be dumped, saving only a small selection of shapes and sizes. As with the bottles, corks by the bag-full were more than plentiful, but I managed to pass on lots of these to homemade wine enthusiasts, just keeping a wide selection for the cork drawers in the dispensing bench. To go with these bottles and corks I came across a few cork-presses which were essential in a busy pharmacy for, although corks were made to standard sizes, the mouths of bottles were not always the same and a quick press of the cork ensured a tight fit.

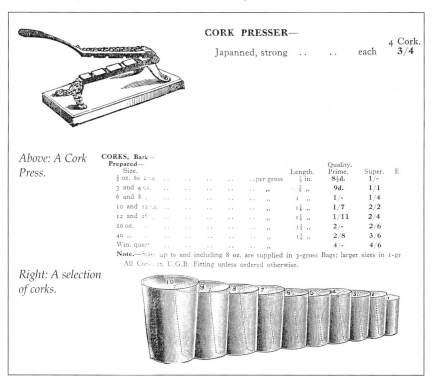

CORK PRESSER—

Japanned, strong .. .. each

4 Cork.
3/4

Above: A Cork Press.

CORKS, Bark — Prepared—

Size.							Length.	Quality. Prime. 8½d.	Super.	E
½ oz. to 2 oz.	..	..	..	..	..per gross	⅝ in.	8½d.	1/-	
3 and 4 oz.	..	..	..	..	,,	⅞ ,,	9d.	1/1	
6 and 8 ,	..	..	..	..	,,	1 ,,	1/-	1/4	
10 and 12 oz.	..	..	..	..	,,	1¼ ,,	1/7	2/2	
12 and 16 ,,	..	..	..	..	,,	1¼ ,,	1/11	2/4	
20 oz.	..	..	..	..	,,	1¼ ,,	2/-	2/6	
40 ,,	..	..	..	..	,,	1½ ,,	2/8	3/6	
Win. quart	..	..	..	..	,,		4/-	4/6	

Note.—Sizes up to and including 8 oz. are supplied in 3-gross Bags; larger sizes in 1-gross
All Corks in U.G.B. Fitting unless ordered otherwise.

Right: A selection of corks.

Left: Making the pill mass in the pill mortar.

Above: Rolling the pill mass into a 'pipe' of the required length before cutting into pills.

Left: Rounding the pills on each other on the pile tile.

Other items of dispensing equipment were found in certain pharmacies, such as suppository moulds, cachet machines, powder folders, etc, as illustrated in W A Jackson's book *The Victorian Chemist and Druggist*, Shire Publications Ltd, Album 80.

Before medicine administration in tablet form came along, pills were the most common form of solid drug use and all the older pharmacies had their pill machines. At one stage I had accumulated fourteen sets in assorted sizes, but then antique collectors became interested in them and they were no longer present when I arrived on the scene, as was happening with most of the attractive, coloured ointment and drug jars. The prescribing of pills was common up to the 1940s, but gradually the use declined and although I had to make some in the 1950s I had no call on my pill-making skills after 1960. Pill-making equipment consisted of pill machines, double-ended mortar and pestle, boxwood rounder, pill spatula, boxwood silverer, earthenware varnishing pot and a graduated pill tile – the latter item seldom being available (*see colour plate on page 66*).

Items that often turned up in drawers in dispensaries were plaster irons, with which I was then unfamiliar, even in my student days, but these plain, rusty iron objects with wooden handles gradually became more significant, as I began to find many different sorts of packages labelled 'plasters' – which I likened to hard misshapen sausages, wrapped in cloth or paper – and other flat packages, which were obviously more recent and ready-prepared sheets of calico and linen spread evenly with plaster. The following quote from the 1923 *British Pharmaceutical Codex* describes plasters (Emplastra).

Plaster masses are intended to be spread upon leather, calico, or other suitable material, the plaster so produced being designed either to maintain a medical substance in close contact with the skin, to act as a protective, or to assist in the approximation of the edges of wounds. The material usually employed for supporting the layer of plaster-mass is a rather thin white leather, known as 'plaster skin'; it should be smoothed with a hot iron before spreading the plaster. Plasters are frequently cut from a large piece, which has been spread by machinery. In spreading plasters, the mass should be melted over a water-bath and precautions taken to avoid destroying alkaloidal principles or dissipating volatile matters by excess of heat. The plasters-mass should be spread as thinly as possible upon the supporting material, a margin of the material at least half an inch wide being left bare, to avoid extension of the mass over the edge of the plaster.

Plasters having a basis of lead, resin, or soap plaster require to be warmed before application to the body; those having an india-rubber base basis adhere closely by the warmth of the body. Plasters intended to raise a blister are made soft in order that they may be easily removed from the vesicated surface; blistering plaster-masses are usually adhesive plaster, the spread upon edges of the latter being warmed before application to the skin. For use in minor surgery and as protective, agents plasters are prepared spread with a solution of isinglass, the usual backing being felt of various thicknesses, linen, muslin and silk; such plasters require to be moistened with warm water before application.

Spreading the plaster with a plaster iron was a very skilled technique, over-heating the iron in the fire, or over the gas ring, could be disastrous to the constituents of the plaster, but it was made easier by using a hollow iron with many tiny gas jets on its surface, which when lit maintained a constant controllable heat.

Left: Melting the solid plaster mass with the heated plaster iron.

Below: Spreading the plaster mass evenly while still hot.

Examples of plasters that I found are Resin Plaster, Belladonna Plaster, Cantharides Plaster, Lead Plaster, Soap Plaster, Mustard Plaster, Menthol Plaster and Galbanum Raster, all of which now reside in the plaster drawer of one of the drug-runs in the Bridewell Museum. Unlike the self-adhesive antiseptic dressing plasters of today, used for cuts and abrasions, these plasters were used for many different purposes. In the 1885 British Pharmacoepia there were fourteen official plasters, in the 1932 British Pharmacoepia only four were included and by 1948 they had all gone. Three basic plasters used were Lead, Soap, and Resin (known as Adhesive Plaster), into which other ingredients were incorporated and their uses varied from pain relief for Rheumatism, Lumbago and painful joints, etc to treating mosquito bites, and bee and wasp stings.

Among the general accessories such as pens, rulers, ink bottles, blotting paper, rubber stamps, etc that often cluttered the writing desks in dispensaries, I came across several personal items that had been part of the pharmacist's everyday life – several pairs of spectacles, a pair of pince-nez, numerous ashtrays and pipes, a tobacco tin, foreign coins – mostly Irish pennies or tokens passed over the counter unnoticed I suspect – and even a pair of black woollen mittens from the shop with no heating! Bundles of keys on rings or pieces of string were at many locations and one of them that I brought back with me was large, rusty, obviously old and looked as if it belonged to a massive church door lock. Perhaps the pharmacist had been a church warden! A few had been Air-Raid Wardens as indicated by the gas masks and steel helmets, marked with their initials, found hanging on the back of cupboard doors – so why not a church warden? I was intrigued to find in a dispensary cupboard a pair of well-worn tartan carpet slippers and a pair of black rubber boots with a red patch from a cycle repair outfit on one heel. I removed them discreetly as I could not imagine the circumstances of their use in a pharmacy. Possibly there was some connection with the Air-Raid Warden's gas mask.

I was initially surprised to find large metal syringes and enamel bowls hidden away in backroom cupboards, but the frequency with which I came across these items made me realise that syringing of ears was a service undertaken by many pharmacists. There were also many small, glass, ear syringes in priced boxes for home use; in one storeroom I found an unopened box of six, small, round enamel bowls, the box labelled 'For personal hygiene', but as these were next to boxes of douche cans, perhaps they were not intended to be used just for ear-syringing!

Chapter Six

Nostrums
and Secret Remedies

— ❖ —

IN all of the pharmacies that I visited, I found a selection of the pharmacist's own 'special remedies' (Nostrums) and, occasionally, I was lucky enough to find a record of the ingredients and method of preparation of these items. Usually hand-written in a much-thumbed pocket-book (*see colour plate on page 67*), they were kept somewhere away from prying eyes, one such place being the pocket of the proprietor's white coat, which was an ideal place for a quick reference. Most of the items in the book were those which the pharmacist had found over the years to be effective and better than any proprietary product, not necessarily his own formulae, but quite often derived from standard reference formulae books, such as those produced by the publishers of the *Chemist and Druggist*. Volume One being pharmaceutical formulas of known, admitted and approved remedies from former editions and from the *Chemist and Druggist Diaries*, and Volume Two being the Chemists' Recipe Book of formulae for household, culinary, horticultural, agricultural, photographic, veterinary, toiletries and many other

Some preparations were given different names, so that it could be claimed as being only available from one pharmacy.

PINE-OZONE.
[10585.

P.J.F.]
DIRECTIONS.
Ten to twenty drops to be inhaled from the handker-
chief immediately on the appearance of symptoms
of Cold in the Head, Influenza, Coughs, Nasal Catarrh, in
fact all Throat and Chest Affections. A few drops on
cotton wool placed in the cavity of a hollow tooth will give
immediate relief from severe Tooth-ache. For Nas
Catarrh, put 2 or 3 drops on a small piece of cotton wo
and insert in the nostril. For Whooping Cough, pla
20 drops on the pillow and nightdress, and let Ch
inhale freely.

W. JONES & CO
The Russell Pharmacy,
134, SOUTHAMPTON ROW, W.C.

PINOZONE.
(P.J.F., 10585.)
Ten to twenty drops to be inhaled from the Inhaler
immediately on the appearance of symptoms of Cold
in the Head, Influenza, Coughs, Nasal Catarrh, in fact all
Throat and Chest Affections. A few drops on cotton wool
placed in the cavity of a hollow tooth will give immediate
relief from severe Tooth-ache. For Nasal Catarrh, three
drops on a plug of cotton wool placed into the nostril is
a sure cure.
For Croup and Whooping Cough, sprinkle a few drops
on the Child's bib, and also under the pillow so that it
may be inhaled during sleep.

PREPARED ONLY BY
R. T. JEFFS, Chemist,
The Parkwood Pharmacy,
Telephone: 587.   **BOSCOMBE.**

everyday preparations. The first edition of these books was published in April 1898 by *The Chemist and Druggist* in London and new editions were published every few years, which accounted for the fact that I came across many different editions, according to the age of the pharmacy, and several ninth and tenth editions (1914–1934) from pharmacies of the 1930s. Some of the preparations from the formularies were made up and given different names, so that it could be claimed to be available from one particular pharmacy only, eg adverts from two different chemists using the formula **PJF 10585,** with the slight variation in name, for it to be claimed as being available only from that pharmacy.

A prescription in a pharmacist's pocket book caught my attention – it was a night cream for ladies with sensitive skin and was labelled **Ceratum Humidum**. Instructions for making it up were: "Take one large pot of Cold Cream, stir in five drops of Oil of Lemon and transfer to an ointment pot". In another pocket-book, dated 1900, was the following definition; 'Dead Drunk' exists when drunkards continue drinking, but when the alcohol imbibed ceases to be absorbed and the blood presents the proportion of one part alcohol to 195 parts of blood, after which death is caused by further drinking.

'Nostrums' from a pharmacist's pocket book revealed these formulae for Nipple Liniment and a cream, purported to be a remedy for freckles.

Many pharmacist's own products became quite well known and were sent all over the country to people who had bought them from the pharmacy, or had been recommended to try them. In a backroom cupboard at one of the more interesting pharmacies I found boxes full of leaflets, literature, empty tins and printed cartons for a special ointment, alongside a thick bundle of letters, tied with bright-yellow string, from customers requesting further supplies, each one having enclosed a postal order to include postage and packing. Some of these letters gave details of what the ointment was being used for and how good it was – testimonials in fact, or were they hoping for discount on their next purchase! Quite often the pharmacist sold preparations made by his local colleagues where the demand warranted it, such as **Collins Elixir**, originally made in the Norwich pharmacy and sold by many local chemists. The most popular preparations had their own labels and packaging, and were sold over the counter by request, or recommendation, but the 'specials' were individually prepared and handed out with appropriate instructions to the customer by the pharmacist. These 'chemist-own' remedies covered a wide range of formulae, most commonly cough mixtures, indigestion mixtures, creams and ointments, but included many things specific to a particular pharmacy like tonics, corn cures, freckle lotions, hair restorers and chilblain preparations. Among my own 'specials' that I prescribed for local customers, the most frequently called for was a cough mixture labelled with very detailed instructions as to its dosage, which I carefully explained had to be adhered to exactly, to make the medicine work. Likewise, an unperfumed hand-cream for bricklayers' use in wintertime had instructions on the jar for it to be put into the cracks in the skin of the hands in the evening and left for at least ten minutes before massaging in. I am sure the detailed instructions made the products work. Requests for medicines were often scribbled on paper and presented in the shop by a child. Although these notes were seldom difficult to read, their grammar and spelling were often amusing and I acquired a considerable number of these over the years, the enclosed notes (*see page 58*) being the more lucid and readable.

Some of the more unusual items I remember being asked for in my early days in pharmacy are as follows:

Hicory Picory Pills – Pills of Heira Picra BPC, made from Socotrine Aloes and Canella bark, and used as a purgative for constipation.

Opodeldoc – Another name for Soap Liniment, made from Soft Soap, Camphor, Rosemary Oil and Alcohol, and used as a mild counter-irritant for sprains, bruises and rheumatic joints.

please make me up
a bottle of KAIOLEN
ZED.
small size please.

please have you any Vitamin
Tablets, (I feed my family
the correct food but I do not
get the Vitamins I require, the
vitamins for vitatality bright eyes
etc. nothing like yeast vite as
I have

Sebbix
pkt B
pkt R
(green

Would you please make
me a 2/6 Bottle of Stomach
medicine as my husband
cannot keep anything down.
I have had it before
its Brown & white

Please would you send a syringe for
original Dootching
1/9.1

would you please send something
to act quite for constipation
something to start it, been in bed
for one week want to go but cannot
Thank you.

58

Dragon's Blood – Sang Draconis, a crimson resin from Sumatra, used for colouring lacquers and varnishes.

ABC Liniment – a liniment made from Aconite Liniment, Belladonna Liniment and Chloroform, and used for rheumatism, neuralgia and sciatica.

Buckho Leaves – Buchu Leaves, used for making an infusion for taking to relieve cystitis.

Steel Wine – made from Iron Wire steeped in Sherry, used as an astringent tonic.

Yo Ho Oil – Japanese Peppermint Oil (Po-ho-yo)

Elastic Accordion – Flexible Collodion, artificial skin used to cover small cuts and abrasions.

My most embarrassing experience with customers was in my first few days in retail pharmacy. A man walked into the shop and asked to speak to the chemist – this should have told me something– but when he mumbled a word from the corner of his mouth I could not get what he meant, it sounded something like 'Apprentices', so I asked him what it was for! He glared at me, mouthed a rude word and stormed out of the shop, never to return, as I found out later. All this time the young female shop assistant was trying not to laugh as she knew the man always came into the shop on a Friday and asked for 'Preventatives'. Up till then I had not even been shown the drawer where the contraceptives were kept, but I did not make that mistake again!

Where something was made up and dispensed for an individual person the ingredients, dose and instructions for use were recorded in the Prescription Book and given a number so that a repeat treatment could easily be obtained.

These books, often large leather-bound indexed volumes up to three inches thick with up to 1,000 numbered pages, could contain up to twelve years' prescribing of a pharmacy, of both doctors' and pharmacists' prescriptions, all numbered and priced and listing up to 5,000 items. Weighing four to five kilos each, these massive works of art were relegated to the store room when full, but were available for reference for many years, especially if a particular remedy had been handed down through the family. I was able to rescue many of these old volumes (*see colour plate on page 68*), dating back to the 1860s and they are full of information, giving an insight into the ailments of the local community over a period of time. In the back of one such book was stuck a stamped receipt for ten guineas for life subscription to The Royal Pharmaceutical Society in the name of the pharmacist, and this was dated 1904.

After the introduction of the National Health Service Act in 1948, prescriptions other than from private patients were no longer recorded in the pharmacy and the use of the large prescription books gradually died out, with the few private prescriptions being recorded in much smaller non-specific books. I even found a school exercise book, dated 1952, used for this purpose, although this was an exception.

Many customers treated their own minor ailments, such as indigestion and constipation, with household remedies, buying the ingredients from the pharmacy in small quantities which were pre-packed, such as Senna Pods, Epsom Salts and Glauber Salts (*see colour plate on page 67*), and these I found in considerable quantities in almost all storerooms that I visited, their sale being largely reduced by the onset of free National Health prescriptions.

One of the most popular seasonal requests was for Ginger Wine Essence, usually presented at the pharmacy by a child clutching a torn piece of paper with the ingredients scribbled in pencil – in pennyworths! The formula and number of ingredients varied widely and the prices on the paper bore no relation to cost and quantity of each ingredient, so it was up to the pharmacist, coping with the pre-Christmas rush in the shop, to ascertain what exactly was needed – not an easy task when the customer was a six-year-old with a hand full of pennies. Most recipes were passed down through the family and were for Tincture of Ginger, Tincture of Capsicum, Burnt Sugar Solution and Tartaric Acid, not always spelt correctly and often requiring interpretation and adjustment. The final product was a small bottle of dark concentrated liquid and a packet of crystals. Back home, sugar would be added to water, boiled and strained, then cooled before adding the purchased ingredients, the final product then poured into screw-cap bottles. The proportions of ingredients varied widely according to strength and sweetness required by the individual and some of them were quite pleasant, especially one

A popular seasonal request was for Ginger Wine, with just water and sugar to be added by the customer!

INGREDIENTS FOR GINGER WINE.

P . CADMAN,
Dispensing Chemist,
CHURCH STREET, SHERINGHAM.

that a customer gave me which I found very palatable. When I thanked her for it after Christmas she told me that the essence I had supplied her with was not strong enough, so she had added an equal amount of brandy to it.

In the 1940s, cosmetics and make-up were in short supply and pharmacists were able to make up their own war-time beauty products such as face creams, hand creams, face powder, rouge and liquid-stocking leg make-up. Some of these products were still on storeroom shelves when I visited the premises in the 1960s. On one visit I could not resist examining the bottles of Liquid Stocking; there were dozens of boxes full of them in three different colours, light, medium and dark, and although most of them had dried out completely there were some that were still liquid which I tried on the back of my hand. The light colour was bright yellow, the medium was deep orange and the dark – well, I don't remember seeing any local girls with coffee-coloured legs in the 1940s! I think perhaps these products had gone off slightly over the years.

In 1783, patented, proprietary and recommended medicines intended for human use, and sold as secret remedies, were liable to duty, each package being required to have a Medicine Duty Stamp affixed (*see colour plate on page 68*). The value of the stamp was related to the retail price before addition of the stamp value. In the earlier days, the stamp rates were one-and-a-half pence, threepence and sixpence, according to the price of the item, and as prices increased 'additional duty' stamps were added. Later stamp values were of 3d, 6d and one shilling. There was no disclosure of the full formula, as is now required by law, and the Stamp Acts were repealed in 1941. As the manufacturers of these secret remedies did not disclose the ingredients, there was no safeguard by which these preparations could be assessed from its formula and, consequently, there were preparations of doubtful value for which wildly extravagant claims were made in advertising and on pamphlets accompanying each package. Claims for the cure, or relief, of incurable diseases were often made and although nowadays advertising is even more powerful, the general public is protected from fraud by official regulations requiring declarations of composition on each packet, with proper restraint in advertising proprietary medicines.

The Duty Stamps were in the form of a paper strip covering the closure of the package to act as a seal.

In one of my taped interviews with Guy Robinson (*see Chapter One*), he talked about wildly extravagant claims in advertising for secret remedies for the cure or relief of incurable diseases, and the following are some of the 1920/30s products, with ambitious titles, that he told me about.

Wait and See – Liver Pills.

Barmsule Capsules – LIFE in a Capsule.

Sargol – The great Specific for rounding out the figure.

ODDS-ON Pills, made by the ODDS-ON SPECIFIC Company.
Professor Webster's Celebrated SUSQUEHANNA Pills.

PLASMON – the great Nerve and Brain Food – The Mainstay of Life.

KANDU TABLETS – Compounded to a formula which is regarded as remarkably efficacious by many medical men of knowledge and experience.

More extravagant and fraudulent claims were as follows:

ROULT'S RHEUMATIC REMEDY – A simple, safe and certain, cure for Rheumatism, Lumbago, Sciatica, Neuralgia, Unbroken Chilblains, etc.

BITRO-PHOSPHATE – The 'Curative Powers' of this preparation are explained in a leaflet. A 'Satisfaction or Money Back Guarantee' form is included. **Relief is guaranteed** in many disorders, including Locomotor Ataxy, Paralysis, Diabetes, Bright's Disease and Dropsy. It is recommended also for **Aversion to mental or physical labour**.

SMITH'S ANTI-RHEUMATIC, ANTI-GOUT PILLS – The box contains an absolute guarantee of relief and states that the directors of the manufacturing company include '**All citizens of the USA**'.

Chapter Seven

Chemists' Sundries

— ❖ —

THE vast majority of stock found in the pharmacies came under the heading of 'Chemists' Sundries', covering a wide variety of items other than medicinal and beauty products, the bulk of which were for baby-care and sick-room requisites.

Again, there were some weird and wonderful things discovered in the forgotten areas of cupboards, back rooms and lofts, and part of the joy in finding these was in working out what they were used for. One collapsible wood and string framework initially posed a problem, it was like putting up a deckchair and getting it right more by luck than judgement, but when it was assembled it became a cradle to stop bedclothes from touching the legs of a patient suffering from sores or ulcers. As it had a person's name and price on it, I assumed that it had been bought in specially for a customer but never supplied.

A box containing lengths of smooth, flat pieces of wood in a multitude of sizes did not pose such a problem, they were splints intended for use on fractured limbs, some of which were in pairs and shaped left or right, child or adult. I had visions of a nurse standing at a table sorting through these thirty or more pieces working out whether they were left or right, arm or leg, whilst the patient waited in agony for the correct one to be fitted.

Large earthenware objects such as bedpans, urinals and inhalers were often found in the more isolated regions of pharmacies as their use, and hence sale, decreased. Even in the 1960s I had a stock of several plain white glazed earthenware bedpans which were always out on hire for home confinements.

Earthenware Inhalers were often attractively decorated with designs, mostly in blue or black, with instructions for use, and there were many different shapes, which made them collectors' items, but after a few years I did not come across them in the pharmacies that I visited.

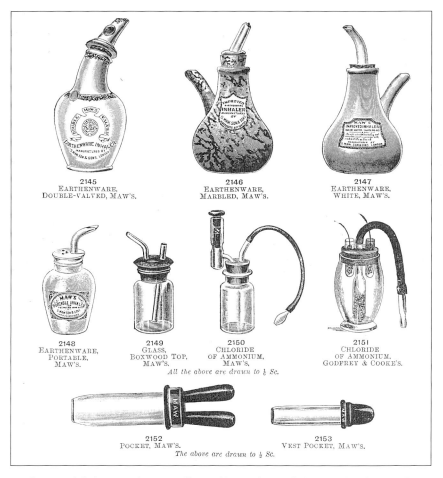

Earthenware inhalers soon became collectors' items, due to their attractive designs. From S Maw, Son & Sons Price List of 1903.

Accompanying the bedpans in their resting places, I sometimes found stone hot-water bottles of various sizes and designs, but these also soon became collectable as they were replaced by rubber ones. Large quantities of rubber hot-water bottles were encountered, possibly because of the large discounts that were given on bulk initial orders. Ordered in late summer in quantities of many dozens, it was not surprising that after a mild winter there were many left over and, as central heating became more popular, the demand for hot-water bottles was not there.

Inhalers in the form of metal bronchitis kettles were not very attractive objects and many were found rusting away where they had been discarded. These small thin metal vessels with no lids had a very long

Above: A selection of weights; which came in a variety of different shapes and sizes, the smaller ones were made of brass and the larger of iron.

Below: Before the days of Sellotape; anything from the dispensary had to be wrapped in white paper, tied and sealed.

Above: Following a casual enquiry, a pharmacist produced a selection of bronze mortars from a back room.

Below: Pill-making equipment; a pill machine, double-ended mortar and pestle, earthenware varnishing pot and graduated pill file – the latter being seldom available.

Pharmacist's usually kept their own special remedies, hand-written, in a well thumbed pocket book – an ideal place for quick reference.

Below: Many customers treated their own minor ailments, buying the ingredients in small packets from the pharmacy.

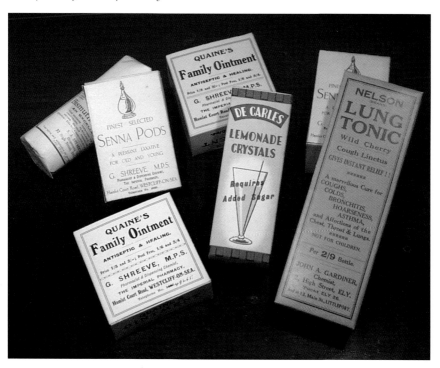

When something was made up and dispensed for an individual person the ingredients, dose and instructions were recorded in the Prescription Book.

These were, as often as not, leather-bound indexed volumes with a large number of pages and could contain up to twelve years of pharmacy history.

Below: After 1783, all patented, proprietary and recommended medicines for human use were required to have a Medicine Duty Stamp attached.

There was no disclosure of the full formula, as is now required by law, and the Stamp Acts were repealed in 1941.

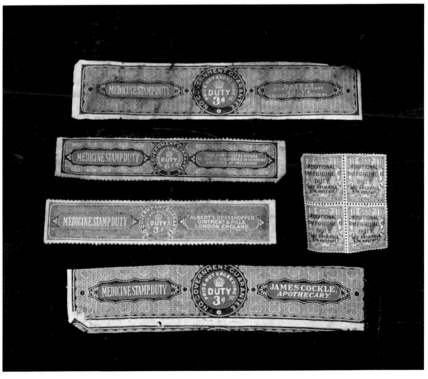

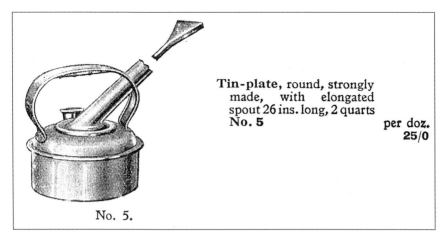

Tin-plate, round, strongly made, with elongated spout 26 ins. long, 2 quarts
No. 5

per doz.
25/0

No. 5.

A metal bronchitis kettle, not an attractive object, generally found where it was discarded in a rusty state.

spout ending in a flattened fantail. In use they were filled with water through a small funnel in the top of the kettle, into which medicaments could also be added. Placed on a stove or fire and heated, the steam and medicament issued from the spout, and with the use of a towel over the head the steam could be inhaled.

Another metal inhaler used in the sick room was very popular due to its convenience and was used a lot in the 1930s for children suffering from whooping cough – says he, remembering it well! It consisted of a metal canister with a night-light in the bottom and an absorbent block or small metal tray in the top which contained an antiseptic liquid to be vapourised. The air in the room became impregnated with the vapour which was inhaled and gave relief to the bronchitis or other respiratory disorder. The one that I remember clearly was a **Wright's Coal Tar Vapouriser**, more of these than any other sort were encountered. Similar to these inhalers in shape and style were metal fumigators, but these were not intended to be used with anyone in the room, they were more intended to kill pests and used such things as nicotine and formaldehyde. One of these was the **XL All Amateur Vapourising Fumigator** which contained lead-sealed poison bottles of 37% liquid nicotine, labelled as "obtainable from all nurserymen, seedsmen, florists and garden sundriesmen everywhere"!

Another item for use in the sick-room was a food-warmer, which also used a metal holder with a decorated earthenware or glass night-light holder in the bottom, and a decorated glazed earthenware jug and lid in the top. Although I found several of the metal holders, complete sets

valuable
Antiseptic
Constituents of
WRIGHT'S
COAL TAR
SOAP.
By means of
this simple
appliance
a carefully
regulated
stream of
Antiseptic
Tar Vapour
can be obtained.
Invaluable for
Whooping Cough
Influenza
Croup
and all
affections
of the
Respiratory
Organs.
WRIGHT'S
COAL TAR INHALER
VAPORIZER
3/6 each
packed in box.
WRIGHT, LAYMAN & UMNEY, LTD.
Proprietors of
WRIGHT'S
COAL TAR SOAP
Southwark, London. S.E.

The Wright's Coal Tar Vapouriser, used for treating children with whooping cough in the 1930s.

were rare as the earthenware items were attractive and collectable. The one that I came across most often was a **Clarke's Food Warmer** (*see colour plate on page 85*), which was a glazed earthenware jug with handle and spout, sitting in a metal water container slotted into a metal framework under which was an earthenware Pyramid Night-Light holder, like a small saucer, surrounded by a grooved domed glass chimney. All earthenware parts were covered with black printed advertising.

To me, while in my teens, a toothbrush was just a toothbrush, but as I progressed in retail pharmacy I found that, to ascertain a customer's requirements, I had to ask: "Nylon or Bristle, Hard, Medium, or Soft?" Little did I realise the range of brushes that I was later to encounter in all those drawers and boxes. An entry in a 1932 wholesale chemist price-list for toothbrushes illustrates this well;

Hand-made by fifty-two special processes. Best London rigid bone handles. Silvered, wired and cemented. Eleven patterns, three textures. Serrated tufts, sterilized open set bristles. Colour identification spots on handles.

Another entry in the same price list states;

Strong handles of generous size, made of beautiful coloured celluloid, six colours, ten patterns, various textures, open set bristles. Retail 9d to 1s 9d.

The types of bristle were listed as Badger Hair, Goat's Hair, Grey Bristle, Black Bristle and White Bristle (hog or pig), and there were also rubber-headed toothbrushes. Although I did not find all these variations there was a considerable number of types, including the odd denture brush, and of course nail-brushes in wood, bone, celluloid and nylon.

While on the subject of brushes, shaving-brushes also appeared, made from different materials, from simple wooden handles to more expensive looking porcelain ones, with bristles made from badger or hog. In one dispensary desk I found two white, shaped porcelain handles in pristine condition, but with no bristles, and at another location there was a cardboard box full of cheap shaving-brushes with wood-worm holes in the handles. Wooden nail-brushes were also found in quantity, but those made from bone and celluloid were seldom seen, unlike the more modern coloured nylon varieties on card display units which were found at most places.

I was surprised that I did not find any hair-brushes, but as they were relatively expensive I suppose they were not stocked in large numbers, unlike hair-combs, which were everywhere, mostly on display cards, and again made from a variety of materials; eg Black Buffalo Horn, Yellow Horn, Celluloid, Grained Ivory, Shell Horn (Imitation Tortoiseshell) and Vulcanite, many of which were made in France.

Whenever I found Surgical Trusses or Elastic Hosiery it took me back to my early days when I had no experience of these, and to be presented with prescriptions for these which required measurements was somewhat daunting. Being in my late 20s, confronted by a portly gentleman in his 70s, the sight of him lowering his trousers and long white underpants in the dispensary filled me with panic, but he very kindly assisted me in undoing the buckle on his somewhat frayed, and not too clean truss, and showing me how to take the measurements. Where the trusses, consisting mainly of elasticated webbing, were intended for supporting hernias of the abdominal wall the measurements were relatively easy to take, but where the hernia was lower down, tact and warm hands was required, but more often than not the patient knew what size was required, thankfully. Now that hernia operations are common these trusses are seldom encountered.

Elastic hosiery giving support for varicose veins came in One Way Stretch or Two Way Stretch and were woven from elasticated cotton or nylon thread, and taking measurements for these could also be embarrassing as the majority of prescriptions were for ladies. Many would take their own measurements but older ladies living on their own were not able to do this and hence had to rely on my 'expertise' and integrity. One lady I fitted with a support stocking left the shop quite happily, but returned the next morning, limping badly with the use of a walking stick. Apparently, while removing the stocking at night, she fell and banged her healthy leg on a chair making it bleed, and she had come for me to put a suitable dressing on it. She assured me that the stocking fitted perfectly and was comfortable. Phew!

Surgical dressings appeared everywhere I went, in drawers, cupboards, tea-chests or on shelves and I must admit that I collected rather more than I could find room for, especially the larger packs of gauze and cotton wool, which I tended to use as packing material for the more fragile items. As with many other sundries, the range of dressings was large, from small finger bandages up to large rolls of cellulose wadding used for mopping up and absorbing excess fluids.

The range of impregnated gauzes available was impressive. There was Picric gauze, Cyanide gauze, Carbolic gauze, Iodoform gauze, Sublimate gauze, Salicyclic Acid gauze and Sal Alembroth gauze, all in sealed

---

Report on the use of red flannel bandages.

Pettigrew (On Superstitions connected with Medicine and Surgery, 1844) says that properties were formerly attributed to certain medicines on the basis of their -colour. Red was a colour associated with heat (as white was with cold) and hence in humoral medicine became associated with the blood. On this basis, red flowers were given for diseases of the blood, as yellow for diseases associated with yellow bile or the liver. Pettigrew says that red flowers such as mulberry and pomegranate were used in the treatment of smallpox; it is probably this same tradition which influenced John of Gaddesden to treat Edward II's son for smallpox by wrapping him in 'scarlet red' cloth. (Rosa Anglica). The same treatment was used, with less success, on the Emperor Francis I in 1765 and seems to have been current in Japan, again for members of the royal family (Wraxall, Memoirs, Kaempfer, History of Japan).

There is another tradition, more closely allied to folk-medicine proper, which is probably more directly connected with the survival of red flannel bandages into the twentieth century. C.J.S. Thompson (The Hand of Destiny, 1932), with others, points out that red as a colour has 'many and peculiar virtues'. As well as its association with heat, it has sacred and regal associations and is considered in folk-medicine of various parts of the world as the colour most effective against evil spirits. Thompson and G.W. Black (Folk Medicine, 1883) both note that in the Highlands and Ireland, red is (or was) used to prevent ill-wishing; they attribute this in part to its being sacred to Thor. The use of red flannel (as a specific against whooping cough, for instance) appears in this context. Cockayne (Saxon Leechdoms) reports similar uses; red flannel was considered as a preventitive for rheumatism, and as recently as the early part of the last century strips of scarlet cloth were reported to be on sale in Fleet Street for use in wrapping up the throats of scarlet fever victims. (Notes and Queries, 5th ser, vol.xi, p.166). In all these cases, the virtue of the treatment seems to have been in the colour rather than in the material used; red worsted and red silk (the latter as a charm against nosebleed) appear in folk-medicine in a similar context.

packets with no indication as to their use. The common rolls and packets of plain absorbent gauze, plain lint and boric lint were found everywhere with the various grades of cotton wool – surgical dressings were important stock items of all pharmacies.

An unusual item was found that dated back to the early 1900s, this was a small number of red-flannel bandages that I could not think had any significance in being red, but the report on the opposite page I found very interesting.

Baby care has always been an important section of pharmacy life and this was brought home to me on more than one occasion by the volume of baby items that appeared from nooks and crannies.

While investigating the attic of a rather dilapidated building I found a large sealed cardboard box on top of an old tin trunk. On trying to remove the box it split open and scattered 144 boat-shaped glass feeding bottles all over the floor. I took four only, and left the tin trunk. Similarly, at another location in the inevitable outside shed, I found large cartons – a shed full in fact – of National Dried Milk, all dated sometime in the 1950s. After a minute's pause I just closed the door on it all and went upon my way. More modern feeding bottles in their own cartons with perished rubber teats were commonplace and did not receive much attention as I had limited space to display the wide choice of manufacturers – and I remember what a chore it was keeping a large range of bottle-teats, especially those packed in bubble-pack strips that could never be stored satisfactorily.

Bottle-brushes, tied in bundles, large and small, and bottles of sterilizing liquid, with or without measures, were found in most shops and added to the picture of how important baby care was, and still is, to pharmacy.

Nursing and sick-room requisites were found in small numbers, such as Breast Relievers, Nipple Shields and Feeding Cups, but an unexpected find, on coat-hangers on the inside of a cupboard door, was an assortment of rubber air-rings, used to prevent bed-sores in bedridden patients. They were all perished and I'm sure the smell kept the mice away.

A representative of a Wholesale Chemists Sundries firm called on me one day and asked if I was interested in buying some treen. His firm had taken over an obsolete business, originally trading in the 1930s, and had found several boxes full of wooden objects in the attic of the building in Kent. Although this was not in East Anglia, and not from a pharmacy, I agreed that I would like to see some samples. When they arrived I was amazed at the workmanship of these small turned boxwood objects with fine screw tops. There were four sizes of menthol cone-holders, an Anal Ointment Introducer and a pill-rounder. I agreed to take all that were available. Imagine my surprise when a tea-chest full arrived by carrier – there were several hundred items and the cost was far more than I had anticipated. However, over the years, large numbers have been distributed to friends and collectors – they made good presents, especially the **Anal Ointment Introducers** (*see colour plate on page 85*). I was glad that these objects were not around when I first qualified, as I found it hard enough explaining to customers that suppositories had to be removed from the silver paper before use and were not to be swallowed!

In the 1930s, bath salts made from crystalline Sodium Carbonate became very popular and the popularity continued right through the war years into the 1950s, with many pharmacies preparing and packing their own, which was a relatively simple operation of adding the required colour and a suitable perfume to the clear colourless crystals and shaking vigorously until well mixed. The job of weighing and packing the crystals into cardboard drums was usually given to the apprentice, or the most junior shop assistant. By the time I arrived on the premises the bath salts were somewhat old and had deteriorated into a white speckled powder, which I took home and used to clean the drains.

Chapter Eight

Advertising Material

— ❖ —

ADVERTISING was an important factor in pharmacy quite early on, even in the seventeenth century, but the examples that I came across were dated from about 1870 onwards, and I had not realised just how many different forms of advertising were present until the collection was well under way.

The majority of advertising material that I found was in the form of coloured cardboard showcards in all shapes and sizes, usually discarded and put out of the way waiting to be disposed of – which they never were, thankfully. Some were used inside cupboards as stock cards, using the plain backs of the cards for listing the contents, while other thinner paper adverts were used to cover shelves, or line the drawers of the drug-runs, instead of newspaper. One drawer of a drug-run, from which the name had been removed and the wooden knob broken, was lined with part of a newspaper dated 10 March 1863, recording various court cases. One in particular caught my eye concerning a man who was arrested by a policeman in the vicinity of an unoccupied house from which a quantity of lead had been removed from the roof. He was charged with possession of 7lb of lead, concealed under his guernsey frock, the piece exactly matching the missing part from the nearby unoccupied house. He was found guilty and sentenced to be kept in penal servitude for four years. On the side of that same drawer were a number of chemist's labels with the date that the drawer was filled and the name of the person concerned. The earliest label was dated 6 November 1859, followed by consecutive labels from 1872, 1890, 1915, 1919, 1920 and 1927. Whatever was kept in that drawer was not replenished very often, but the drawer has been kept and is in a cupboard at the museum.

Where newspaper was used for packing or lining drawers, etc, I saved it all for reading later. One batch of *Norwich Mercury* from 1805–1825 contained many adverts for patent medicines obtained from Norfolk pharmacies, such as the following for **Hallam's Antibilious Pills** on the 2nd of May 1814:

"This safe and useful preparation is justly esteemed for its agreeable and certain operation, by which it effectually removes all Inaction or Obstruction of the Stomach and Bowels, whether arising from Bile, Indigestion, Flatulency, or Cold, Sickness at Stomach, Head Ache, etc. It operates by dislodging acrid bile or other crudities retained in the intestinal canal, and acts as an alterative to the system generally. Its action is particularly adapted to *persons of Bilious Habits*, and those of sedentary lives, where a sufficient action of the bowels is not kept up, and crudities in those organs are frequently producing pains and distentions, headaches, languor, and giddiness, or a sense of weariness and oppression. A single trial will fully convince the patient of their efficacy. *The worst cases of Bilious or Sick Head Aches are certainly removed by a single dose*, and in a much shorter time than could be credited, but from experience. The Proprietor thinks it proper to remark, they will be found not only to act without pain or uneasiness, but to leave the body, after their immediate action ceases, free from that costive state which generally succeeds the operation of laxative medicines. Sold wholesale and retail by E. Edwards, 66 St Paul's Churchyard, London; Price 2/9d and 4/6d per box. Retail also by Bacon, Kinnebrook and Co; and Mrs Bowen, Norwich; Beart and Thompson, Yarmouth; Shalders, Holt; Finch, Swaffham; White and Grounds, Wisbech; and all dealers in medicines".

Other adverts in this batch of newspapers were for Trusses, Toothpowder, Hickman's Pills and Diuretic Drops, obtainable from many listed outlets – not all pharmacies – all with rather exaggerated claims as to their effectiveness.

I soon got into the habit of not throwing away packaging material of any kind. Most cardboard boxes, tins and wooden boxes had been reused as containers for a variety of items and when sorted out the rusty Ovaltine tins were thrown away, the Allenbury's Glycerin and Blackcurrant Pastilles tins were retained, and the cigarette and tobacco tins were given to a collector.

One of the chores I disliked most in the pharmacy was arranging window displays, which usually took all day to complete in between serving customers, but as I found my staff were far more capable of doing this, I tended to leave them to it. The best layouts were constructed by firms' own window-dressers who brought everything with them to promote their products – showcards, dummy packs, display cartons and assorted background cloth and paper. These window displays were

Not confined to showcards, advertising started outside the pharmacy with painted metal signs, as seen here at the Stradbroke, Suffolk, premises of J H Corbyn, 1929–1934.

usually kept in position for only a short time, after which all the material was removed and put into a storeroom to leave the window space for the next display. After a while this material accumulated into large quantities of cardboard, paper, etc and, although many of the pharmacies had a regular clear-out of the excess, some shops never seemed to have got round to sorting it out. These places were the source of some of the best posters and adverts that I found.

I can verify that cardboard in quantity is heavy; I found out the hard way when I tried moving a thick pile of showcards from a high shelf and suddenly found myself on my back on the floor covered in dusty cardboard and a woodworm-riddled shelf! If that was not bad enough, there was not a single showcard worth saving! Dusting myself down, coughing and sneezing, I just picked myself up, left the room and closed the door behind me.

One pile of discarded showcards I found under a bench in a storeroom were interesting in that they were obviously home-made, more than likely during the 1939-1945 period. They were made from sheets of thick cardboard, covered with wallpaper of a very subdued mottled-brown colour with words made from cut-out strips of black paper or stencilled brown lettering, the whole covered in cellophane, most of which had perished. Not very inspiring, but better than nothing in the circumstances, I suppose. The best preserved, ie, not distorted or damaged by mould or damp were as follows;

Elixir of Camphor – The real cure for colds, 1/1d and 2/-
Selways Cold & Influenza Cure – 1/1d and 2/-
Pile Ointment – Gives rapid relief, 1/2d
Corn Famine – Gives immediate foot comfort, 10d

Advertising was not confined to showcards and posters, it started outside the pharmacy with painted metal signs, but the biggest impact must have been where the whole outside walls of the shop were covered with advertising. Shop windows were the most obvious place for pharmacies to advertise, with products such as Kodak films often being incorporated into the shop front as a permanent feature, while inside the shop were many semi-permanent displays made of glass, porcelain, plaster and metal, all incorporating the name of the company supplying them. As these items were attractive-looking they soon became

At the pharmacy of F S Cullen, Magdalen Road, Norwich, exterior advertising was extensive, with the outside walls receiving more than their fair share of adverts and even the gates were given a similar treatment.

☞ SOMETHING NEW!

Mothers read this!

IS IT POSSIBLE

To keep your Children's Heads free from Nits and other Parasites? **Yes!** by using

JOHNSON'S ⚜

Nursery

HAIR LOTION

Which is far more effective than any similar preparation offered, besides being a capital Hair Wash and useful dressing, keeping the Hair soft and glossy. An entirely new and original preparation for quickly destroying Vermin in Children's Hair. Its use involves **Instant Death** to all Parasites, and prevents the germination of these troublesome pests.

SOMETHING NEW!

This preparation is entirely free from "Oils" and Grease. The use of Oil for Children's Heads is now almost out of date, and ought to be by all who care to keep their Children's heads clean and free from filth. The above preparation is effective in all cases, and is

NON-POISONOUS

Sold in Bottles, 6d. and 10d. each,

BY THE SOLE MANUFACTURER,

F. INGRAM JOHNSON,

Park Street Pharmacy,

SOUTHEND-ON-SEA.

NURSERY HAIR LOTION

"Instant death for all parasites" was the claim by F Ingram Johnson, of Southend-on-Sea, for this preparation.

collectable items and were targeted by antique dealers before I arrived on the scene. Those that I did manage to obtain had been put away years before and had become part of the general clutter in the back of storerooms that I had to sort out, and several interesting items were found.

The Yardley Dresden Porcelain figure (*see colour plate on page 86*) was highly sought after by antique dealers, but I was able to purchase a few before they were all sold to dealers and collectors. In 1770, the company that was to become the House of Yardley was established when the Yardley family were Lords of the Manor in Thaxted, Essex.

In 1913, the company adopted as its trade mark for all lavender products the Flower Sellers Group, modelled on one of fourteen paintings by Francis Wheatley RA , comprising The Cries of London. In 1919, an extensive advertising campaign was undertaken, commissioning the Dresden porcelain factory to produce the figures which the company then supplied to its select agents for display purposes. If the display unit was broken when in use it was not replaced by another Dresden figure; instead, a hard-rubber copy was supplied, but as these perished on prolonged exposure to sunlight, very few survived over the years and I saw only one in all my travels.

Other less valuable, or desirable, items were found from time to time, such as a Cow & Gate figure of a mother nursing her baby (*see colour plate on page 86*), made from Plaster of Paris, with the lettering "Next best to Breast", and a Parke Davis bust of a black boy wearing a red fez and a brilliant white smile, advertising Euthymol Tooth Paste and made from Gutta Percha. Even the glass change trays were adverts (*see colour plate on page 87*).

A different form of advertising was found in an outside shed on one property where practically everything had gone already. At first glance it appeared to be a thick roll of linoleum tied with string, but on closer examination it turned out to consist of pieces of perished rubber matting, which I initially put on one side but then decided to open out to see if there was anything else inside. There in the centre were three or four small rubber advertising mats in good condition, one for Calvex Ointment (*see colour plate on page 87*), one for Ucal and the others for cigarettes. Leaflets advertising particular products were obviously used extensively, judging by the number of them that were found, many still in the outer wrappings as received from the printer; these were either laid on the counter to be handed out to customers, delivered by hand to local householders, or put in paper bags with customer's other purchases. The paper bags supplied were printed with the name and address of the pharmacy and often the name of a particular product. As these were obtained from the printer in bulk, there were usually so many that I used them for packing around fragile items to prevent breakage on the journey back home.

Chapter Nine

Removal and Collection

— ❖ —

HAVING been to the pharmacies and secured what was available, the removal and collection of the items was the next problem. Where there was room enough in the car everything was packed and brought home the same day, but larger items such as shelving, counters, cabinets, etc, had to be left to be collected later by using a hire van and a driver friend. The one journey that is still fresh in my memory was the removal and collection of items from The Imperial Pharmacy at Westcliff-on-Sea, which formed the bulk of the fittings of the collection.

With two firemen as driver and mate, we left home early on a crisp Sunday morning in February, cramped into the cab of the hire-van, with my wife sitting on my lap. The journey down to Essex was relatively uneventful but slow, we had frequent stops so that I could stretch my legs and recover normal circulation. We also had to stop for refreshments which we had taken with us – trying to manage eating and drinking on the move in such a confined space proved somewhat hazardous, but hilarious all the same.

Having collected the key from the proprietor, who was retiring and closing down his business, our first task was to take everything off the shelves to be packed in cardboard boxes that we had brought with us. While my wife and I were doing this our two friends started to dismantle the fittings using a hammer, hacksaw blade and brute force to separate units joined together by rusty screws.

The 18ft Hunjadi János glass sign (*see colour plate on page 88*) attached to a ceiling beam proved to be rather difficult to remove. As we had no ladders with us, one of the large counters had to be moved into position under the sign to enable us to reach it, with chairs being placed on top of the counter, after clearing the top of cabinets. Before this could be done the lead sink built into the counter had to be disconnected from the water supply, but this was no easy task as there was no sign of a stopcock

Before the large plate-glass sign could be reached, it was necessary to remove the lead sink which was built into the counter, which necessitated isolating the water supply.

anywhere in the shop. Undaunted and with a hammer in each hand, one of the firemen, who was also a plumber, flattened the lead water-supply pipe just above the floorboards in a few seconds, sawed through the flat pipe and turned over the end several times to make a perfect seal, without allowing more than a couple of cupfuls of water to escape. It was fascinating to watch this skilful operation, as I had visions of a flooded shop and a hasty retirement back to Norfolk.

Once the counter had been repositioned, and the shop chairs secured on the top of it, the job of removing the heavy plate-glass in its wooden frame was undertaken. While the two firemen removed the fixings from the girder I was standing on the middle chair supporting the whole frame. Only afterwards did I realise how stupid it really was, if either end had collapsed I could never have held it in position and would have ended up on the floor with my head stuck through the frame and broken glass all around me – and probably with a broken leg! However our luck held and the whole sign was lowered safely and intact, surviving the journey back and its relocation into the Iceni Pharmacy, and finally removing it from there before being repositioned into its final resting place in the Bridewell Museum.

When the sink was being removed from the counter we discovered that there were two taps, hot and cold, both coming from the one main supply pipe which we severed, but there was no way that hot water could ever have been obtained.

On removal of the stained-glass window backs we found that the leaded-glass panes were bent and bowed inwards; we were told that this happened when bombs landed not far away during a war-time raid, although the large plate-glass shop windows did not break and there were no other breakages, unlike properties close by that suffered considerable damage. As each part of the fittings was removed it was carefully stacked in the van in such a way that it could not move, being held in place by the boxes of bottles previously removed from the shelves. As the van was gradually filled, each subsequent item had to be manipulated and other items moved to form a complex jigsaw. One of the conditions we had to abide by was that everything had to be removed and the shop left empty and clean. We thought we had achieved this until I noticed the heavy glass lightshades were still in position. One of the fittings had to be removed from the van to stand on to get to the lights and then the van repacked. We left the lightbulbs! By the time everything was removed from the shop and packed into the van there was not an inch of spare space left and, on securing the back shutter, we realised we were probably over the weight limit. By this time it had been dark for quite a while and we set off slowly with apprehension and four sweaty bodies in the confines of the cab.

Everything was fine until the first roundabout when the van leaned over alarmingly to one side, with all of us leaning in the opposite direction. I'm sure we did not have all the wheels of the van in contact with the road then, but on approaching subsequent roundabouts we all shouted to the driver to slow down, which he did, negotiating the bends at about 10mph. This necessarily slow journey made us rather late in getting back – we still had to stop to relieve our cramped travelling conditions – and as the van had to be returned before 8am on the Monday everything had to removed, stacked in our garage and the van cleared out. As we started to unload the van it began to snow and to hasten the operation our driver rang his brother to come and help. As none of us had eaten anything for a long time my wife kept us going with hot soup and sandwiches, which we ate in the light of Tilley lamps, which were perched on the flat garage roof. We eventually closed the garage doors on our acquisitions at around 3am and the van was returned to its compound.

Although not on quite such a large scale, this operation was repeated several times where large items of fittings had to collected, and very often when the van was not full we were asked to take empty tea-chests, cardboard boxes, etc, for disposal, a request that we could hardly refuse.

By the time we had stored away everything from Westcliff-on-Sea all our storage space had been filled and I had to consider the future of all the materials I had collected so far. With part of my business warehouse packed with boxes, the garage full of shop fittings, with cars standing outside all winter and a large wooden shed next to the house piled high with boxes of bottles full of powders and liquids, the decision to do something about it all became urgent by the summer time when, periodically, there were small explosions inside the shed as the more volatile liquids in tightly stoppered bottles exploded and covered everything else in small glass fragments. It was obvious to me that the most urgent job was to remove from the shed – where the temperature was reaching 90°F (32°C) – all items that were heat-sensitive, but which needed to be preserved. This involved opening and sorting out about fifty boxes, repacking the removed items, which were transferred to my warehouse and all this done early morning and late evening when the chance of being showered with glass was much less. Several boxes had spaces inside where a bottle had originally been and all that remained was powdered glass and fragments of paper labels. The most dangerous part of the operation was handling the bottles of liquid which had solid ground-glass stoppers which had stuck. On the explosion of the bottles, and contents, these stoppers became missiles and did some damage to the inside of the shed, also cracking a couple of panes of glass in the window. The main priority then was to find somewhere to house the whole collection safely.

Left: Another item used in the sick-room was a food-warmer, such as Clarke's Food Warmer, seen here. This consisted of a glazed earthenware jug with handle and spout, sitting in a metal container under which was a night-light, which supplied the heat.

Below: A selection of Anal Ointment Introducers, Pill Rounders and Menthol Cone Holders, which were available in large quantities, so much so that they made good presents to friends and collectors alike!

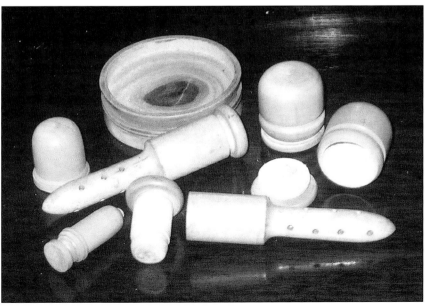

The Yardley Dresden
Porcelain figure was
highly sought-after by
collectors.
  The Flower Sellers
group was adopted as
the company's trade
mark in 1913, although
the original models had
been primrose sellers.

Below: Less valuable,
but still collectable, is
the Cow & Gate model,
in Plaster of Paris, of a
mother nursing her
baby, and also the Gutta
Percha bust from Parke
Davis & Co.

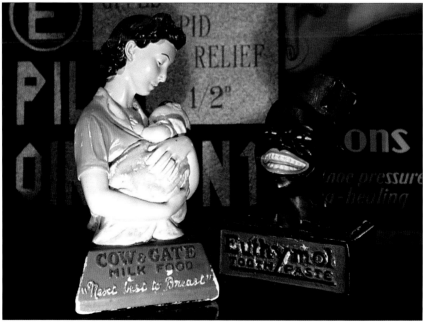

Above: A different form of advertising was discovered in an outside shed. At a first glance it appeared to be nothing more than a roll of linoleum, but upon closer inspection was revealed a collection of small, rubber, advertising mats.

Below: Even the glass change trays were utilised for advertising purposes.

Above: The bulk of the fittings in the collection came from the Imperial Pharmacy at Westcliff-on-Sea in Essex. The 18-foot Hunjadi János glass sign proved rather difficult to remove as it was attached to a beam on the ceiling.

Below: An evening view of the exterior of the completed Iceni Pharmacy, with its own section of roadway and street light!

Chapter Ten

Relocation
and Assembly

— ❖ —

I N 1974, I applied for planning permission to erect a building behind
our house to hold the collection, showing it as a pharmacy museum.
Unfortunately, the local council treated it as an application for a
pharmacy business and a museum open to the general public, and it took
me a year to persuade them that what I needed was a building to house
my own personal collection, open only by invitation to interested people,
and the requirements for public toilets and parking facilities were not
necessary.

The original shop front of Hutchinsons Chemists Ltd, of Whittlesea, Cambridgeshire,
which was originally planned to become the donor for the front of The Iceni Pharmacy,
although a subsequent examination of the frames ruled this out!

The shop front was removed by the shop-fitters, but before collection much of the glass was broken and then a mishap inside the van reduced it to somewhat smaller pieces. The remains were then stacked up against the side of a shed.

From gaining planning permission for the building it then took another year before work could start due to an acute shortage of bricks and by then it was the hot summer of 1976. While waiting for the building materials I heard of a pharmacy in the Fens that was changing its shop front and I was able to obtain the old wooden structure in its entirety, which was removed by the shop-fitters and stored in a backyard for a short while until I could fetch it. Before I could arrange the collection, vandals managed to break most of the glass, but with my trusty fireman friend and the inevitable white hire-van we arrived home with it all in reasonable shape – that is, until the van tilted on a drain-cover by the side of the house and there was a mighty crash inside the van as almost everything collapsed. Removed in somewhat smaller pieces we stood the shop front up against the wooden shed to await its future fate.

Meanwhile, building had commenced and when the footings were being dug out the builder found some embossed-glass medicine bottles from local chemists, which were broken and not worth saving, but it kindled his interest in what we were trying to do. The bricklaying was slowed down by having to soak the bricks in a tin bath of water before laying due to the scorching hot sun. The pitched felt roof had to be completed at night, as when it was started during the day the tar on the felt melted and the sheets just slipped off the roof.

When the old shop front was examined carefully it was found to be held together by multiple layers of paint over soft rotting wood, so it was decided to recreate the whole structure, using the old frames as templates and replacing the glass with curved panes individually made by Pilkingtons – an expense I had not catered for.

We were fortunate to find an enthusiastic carpenter-joiner who meticulously made the wooden frames and door, creating a tool to form the correct curves of the windows.

I had previously measured and drawn all the fittings to arrive at a size of the building to take all that was necessary for a complete shop layout and once all the required pieces were earmarked I was able to dispose of the excess fittings. Most of the large wall units that could not be fitted in our building were supplied to Hackett's of London for refitting a barber's shop in the Victorian style, and several counters and glass cabinets were used by a friend when he opened a shop selling sporting and target guns, and ammunition – a business no longer in existence.

The hot summer of 1976 caused many problems with the building of the pharmacy to house the collection. The bricks had to be soaked to prevent them drying out in the hot sun and then the tar on the roofing felt melted!

91

An enthusiastic carpenter-joiner meticulously fabricated the wooden frames and door, and made a tool to create the correct curvature of the windows.

By November 1976, the building was complete and ready to be fitted out. Again, with my fireman friend Ron Bishop, we borrowed a van from a supermarket to transport counters and fittings from my warehouse on a bright sunny Saturday morning. Unfortunately, while directing the van reversing alongside the house, I managed to get between the van and the house where there was insufficient space, resulting in getting crushed and somewhat flattened. Although my stay in hospital was short, when I returned home I had no desire to go into the building to restart the layout until February 1977. Fitting together the pieces of furniture from different pharmacies I recalled many memories of when I had removed them from their original sites – even the different smells of the fittings reminded me of where they came from, like the tobacco smell inside the desk from Westcliff-on-Sea, the antiseptic smell of the cupboard that held the bedpans for hire, the smell of rubber from the drawers that held air-rings and rubber sheeting and the sickly, heady smell of the glass cabinet that had contained an assortment of perfumes.

By November 1976 the building was complete and ready to fit out.

Gradually everything was dovetailed together and the contents of all the boxes allocated their respective places – many on the shelves or in cupboards where they were originally found. Once more it was time for the Hunjadi János sign to be moved. This time we had adequate ladders and steps; holes were drilled high in the back wall of the pharmacy and the whole sign was lifted into place and secured by large screws – but it was still just as heavy. Little did I think at that time that the whole process of removing and re-positioning the sign (*see colour plate on page 88*) would have to be done a few years later.

To complete the atmosphere once the building was completed, we constructed a small street between the house and the museum, using old materials. Granite sets, originally from Norwich streets, were found at a stonemason's, but as there were insufficient of these we purchased a lorry load of old limestone blocks from Ipswich. A heap of massive granite kerb-edging was found in a lay-by on the outskirts of Norwich and we persuaded the council to let us have what we needed at £1 per piece – naturally we sorted out the pile of stone and picked the longest pieces we could find! Due to the weight of these pieces – many could only be lifted by two people – it took several trips with our car to get what was required.

A council inspector then examined and counted our haul before we started laying the street. In the meantime, we had obtained old street

The Iceni Pharmacy is fronted by a traditional street layout, complete with granite sets and to complete the picture is an elegant, old street lamp which originated, with the sets, from Ipswich.

paving-slabs from Norwich City Highway's Department to complete the street layout. As the granite and limestone sets had to be laid accurately in sand and cement, this job was undertaken by my wife whose fingers were small enough to get between the sets – not so much a labour of love, more like a labour of broken fingernails and many pairs of rubber gloves. To complete the picture we also erected an old iron street-lamp standard which came with the limestone sets from Ipswich.

I spent many cold winter evenings in the pharmacy, well wrapped in coat, scarf and gloves, sorting out items, trying to remember where everything came from and where it was located in the pharmacy of origin. Many times I was momentarily stumped as to where a certain item should be put, but there seemed to be a presence or something showing me what to do. At first it was a bit daunting, but when I got used to it I used to tell my wife that I was going over to the shop to see my friends, but she never brought me more than one cup of coffee at a time!

To complete the collection I felt the pharmacy should have a name and I settled for **The Iceni Pharmacy** as, like Queen Boudica of the Iceni Tribe, I had wandered all over East Anglia for many years, but collecting not pillaging.

In July 1977, I invited Leslie Matthews, the country's leading Pharmaceutical Historian, to open the pharmacy, accompanied by members of the British Society for the History of Pharmacy, local dignitaries, our builders, firemen friends and the press, and from then on I opened the pharmacy by invitation only on my half-day and weekends. Visitors came from far and wide, many having read articles which appeared in professional publications, but the largest group to visit us was twenty German firemen, over on an exchange visit – yes, you guessed it – with our firemen friends, who all arrived in a fire engine to be treated to an English afternoon tea as well as looking at the collection.

The pharmacy was used by several TV companies as a background for plays or topical news subjects; the one that we recall most vividly was when a team from the BBC flew up to Norwich airport in a charter plane, collected two Volvo estate hire-cars and spent all day filming, expecting to be fed and watered. I had to take the day off work to be there, spending most of the time preventing the fittings from being moved around to provide better camera shots. As the TV crew left I was presented with a large bottle of whisky and we then had to clear up all the cigarette ends that had been dropped in any open receptacle on the counters and dispensing bench. When the programme, **Drug Hunters – Poisons that Heal,** was televised, scenes from the pharmacy took up less than five minutes of the total programme This was the last time we invited the media to our house.

By 1982, we began looking for a permanent site for the collection, realising that if anything had happened to me my wife would not be allowed to retain anything containing original contents, thus destroying the whole concept. At first the local museum authorities could not find suitable accommodation for the whole collection, so I tried elsewhere. In Cambridge, one of the chemist shops that I had worked in became vacant and I was approached to see if I would sell part of my fittings to be used to give an old atmosphere to a new venture selling toilet products. Having spent years getting the collection together I did not intend to break it up this way.

Eventually, in October 1984, I was offered the Sea and River room at the Bridewell Museum in Norwich, which was a large enough room to accommodate the collection. Once more we had to remove everything from the cupboards and shelves in **The Iceni Pharmacy** to be packed in boxes, shelving dismantled, fixtures unfastened and everything transported to its new home with the help of our builder, Brian, and his small lorry. We had to use a small vehicle to negotiate the pedestrianised alley, with permission from Norwich City Council to access the museum

Moving the collection to the Bridewell Museum in Norwich took several weekends against the background of deteriorating weather, which did not help! Using a small vehicle as access to the pedestrianised alley outside the museum was restricted, we were able to access the museum on Sundays only.

The pharmacy exhibition in the Bridewell Museum, Norwich.

on Sundays only. The transference took several weekends to complete, by which time the weather was not good and the large pieces of furniture had to be covered with tarpaulins for the short journey, which, on arrival, had to be manhandled by four men, up and over the staircases, carefully avoiding the antique clocks on the walls.

On one Sunday morning journey when going over a bridge, one of the counters which was hanging over the back of the lorry jolted and the end glass door opened and smashed, scattering thick chunks of glass over the road. We stopped a few yards further on and, taking the traditional builder's stiff brush from the frame of the lorry, I tried to sweep the glass into the gutter, but with no red triangle available it was like being at the fair-ground 'Dodgems' with the cars hurtling over the bridge before they could see me, braking and swerving past me as they mouthed "Good morning" to me – at least, I like to think that was what they were saying.

When everything had been removed from the Iceni Pharmacy and transferred to the Bridewell Museum, the Sea and River room was blocked off and the builder and his carpenter then reconstructed the pharmacy, following my chalk marks on the floor. What a relief it was to see the Hunjadi János sign safely in position – and I didn't have to touch it! The pharmacy was constructed so that the shop layout and dispensary could be seen by visitors from behind a glass screen, to ensure that the contents could be preserved. The large amount of money needed to provide this toughened glass screen and doors was raised by the Friends of Norwich Museums and donations from local pharmacists and businesses.

Once everything was nominally in place the pharmacy was opened in June 1985, again by Leslie Matthews, this time joined by Museum officials, Friends of the Museum, Norwich City dignitaries and local pharmacists.

The biggest task was then to come – every item in the collection, which amounted to several thousand, had to be numbered, entered in a register and then transferred onto individual sheets giving all details to be put on the computer. As I was the only one who knew the complete history of everything, the task was mine, with help from several volunteers over the years who carefully numbered each item.

As soon as everything was laid out there was an initial rush by the media to use the setting as a background for various programmes, but once again there was very little respect for the items on view, but by imposing a fee for using the collection the demand gradually ceased. School groups were invited in for demonstrations, initially there was a lot of interest, especially all the different pungent smells and the sight of mercury rolling along the counter in small droplets, but this practice ceased after a while as it became difficult to prevent children from opening drawers and handling items which were fragile or irreplaceable. Cataloguing the collection was completed in 2002 and I hope that sometime in the near future an audio-visual system can be installed to explain what the pharmacy is all about.

Chapter Eleven

Then and Now

— ❖ —

I N pharmacies of today I feel completely lost – gone are the bunsen burners, sealing wax and string, the label drawers with their many compartments for the wide variety of size and type of label, the desk tops, ink and blotters for writing the labels, the label-moistener to save licking the gummed labels, the rack of upturned measures, the brass dispensing scales with Apothecary weights and the neat rows of glass-stoppered bottles of powders and liquids for compounding prescriptions. Instead, today the dispensing bench is dominated by the computer, which produces the required self-adhesive printed label at the touch of a few keys, complete with additional information and instructions on dosage and compatibility with other drugs, while the dispensing shelves are neatly lined with original packs of current prescription drugs, the generic names of which I find hard to pronounce let alone understand, but the complex nature of medicinal drugs these days means that pharmacist's knowledge must be just as extensive with these modern, mostly synthetic preparations, as was that of the previous generation of pharmacists who used naturally-occurring substances to prepare suitable forms of medication.

I have recently been back to the locations of many of the pharmacies I have written about, but, sadly, very few are still trading as such, most properties have changed to other businesses, some of them several times and other places have disappeared completely, being replaced by car-parks, gardens, pedestrian walk-ways and other features of present-day living. Very few single-proprietor pharmacies seem to be trading these days, with large national companies supplying most of the pharmaceutical services.

The illustrations on the following pages are just a few of the places I visited that are still recognisable by their locations.

Above and right: Row & Taylor (Norwich) Ltd were situated to the left of Marks & Spencer, a position which is now occupied by an extension of the department store.

Right: The pharmacy of F S Cullen, situated on Magdalen Road, Norwich was, in the early days, extensively covered with all manner of advertisements, something which it would be hard to visualise with the stringent planning regulations of today.

However, a certain amount of advertising is still permitted, with "It's No Sweat at the Tanning Centre" – "Where the Sun Always Shines", displayed on the premises, which is now a centre for obtaining a suntan!

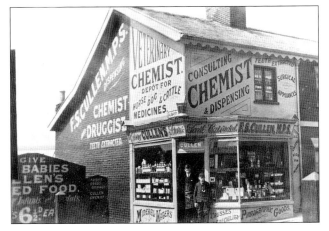

Above: The premises of Gardiner and Lacey, the Guildhall Pharmacy, of No 13 St Giles' Street, Norwich, taken in 1953 – now the home of Norfolk Blinds, specialising in conservatory blinds.

Left: Maddison's Chemist and Druggist shop at Foulsham, near Fakenham in North Norfolk, complete with pony and trap – now a private dwelling.

Appendices

— ❖ —

BELOW is a list of pharmacies that make up the bulk of the collection at The Bridewell Museum, Norwich.

Row & Taylor (Norwich) Ltd, Norwich, Norfolk; Smith & Sons (Norwich) Ltd, Norwich, Norfolk; E R Sayle MPS, Norwich, Norfolk; Chas F Shewell MPS, Cromer, Norfolk; Smith & Wesley (Chemists) Ltd, Downham Market, Norfolk; R J Lines Ltd, Hunstanton, Norfolk; Coleman & Brown, Lowestoft, Suffolk; Wiles & Holman, Felixstowe, Suffolk; The Wolsey Pharmacy, Ipswich, Suffolk; Bobby & Son, Soham, Cambs; J A Gardiner, Ely, Cambs; R Scrafton & Son Ltd, Wisbech, Cambs; S J Shearman MPS, Brightlingsea, Essex; The Victorian Pharmacy, Brightlingsea, Essex; G Shreeve MPS, Westcliff-on-Sea, Essex.

Many of these pharmacies no longer exist.

All the following pharmacies and pharmacists are represented in the collection, some by only one item such as an empty bottle or simply a label.

Arthur Larder MPS, Norwich; E J Bailey, Norwich; Gardiner & Lacey, Norwich; Guy Robinson, Norwich; Maurice French MPS, Norwich; Dewing, Norwich; Robinson & Co, Norwich; Frank Smith & Son (Chemist) Ltd, Norwich; James Cook MPS, Norwich; J Staton MPS, Norwich; D J Hunt MPS, Norwich; E R Veness MPS, Norwich; Russell Margetts MPS, Norwich; Alf J Grand MPS, Norwich; Larder & Whitehead, Norwich; W T Dawson MPS, Norwich; Hurn (Chemists) Ltd, Norwich; James Watson MPS, Norwich; Boots Ltd, Norwich; H E DeCarle Ltd, Norwich; J F Cullen, Norwich; Philip Mason & Son, Norwich; Collins Ltd, Norwich; T B Brittan MPS, Norwich; Norwich Co-op Soc, Norwich; H H Calvert, Norwich; Reads Cash Chemist, Norwich; H A King & Son, Norwich; Caley Pharmaceutical Chemists, Norwich; John Newstead MPS, Sprowston, Norwich; R H Hands, Hunstanton;

Taken in 1900, Hoare's chemists shop in Cromer offers the customer "Prescriptions accurately dispensed", as well as Kodak and Solio photographic products 'kept in stock'.

W H Lenton MPS, Hunstanton; J MacMillan, Hunstanton; W P Hoare, Cromer; F Ruff Ltd, Cromer; D Davison, Cromer; H Oakley MPS, King's Lynn; H T Shewell, Sheringham; P Cadman Ltd, Sheringham; Ebbage, late Owles, Great Yarmouth; Wiles & Holman, late E Gange, Mundesley-on-Sea; James M Weller, Long Stratton; Edward Johnson MPS, Harleston; A E Churchyard, Harleston; R C Hannent, Gorleston-on-Sea; W A Ogden (Chemist) Ltd, Wymondham; I Sharman, Great Yarmouth; Steward & Son, Great Yarmouth; Gostling & Co, Diss; W I Gibson MPS, Diss; Ceres Pharmacy, Swaffham; Boots Ltd, Swaffham; Cooper & Co (Swaffham) Ltd, Swaffham; G Searle, Fakenham; J C Holton, Fakenham; J H Arnall MPS, Aylsham; E Collins Ltd, Aylsham; Rees T Coghlan Ltd, Loddon; Parry & Large, Thetford; H J Bramhall Ltd, Thetford; Oliver & Griston, North Walsham; R M Ling MPS, North Walsham; Edward Peck, Dereham; W M George, Halesworth; S B Allen MPS, Lowestoft; Fryer & Co, Lowestoft; S C Halliday & Co, Lowestoft; Wiggin & Son, Ipswich; Smalley's, Ipswich; D D Coutts MPS, Ipswich; Wolsey Pharmacy, Ipswich; Pain & Bayles, Ipswich; John Betts & Son, Woodbridge; Stearn Bros, Stowmarket; B Shearman, Haverhill; L W Humphries, Laverham;

J H Corbyn, Stradbrooke; A Bollam, Debenham; L I Leeson MPS, Bury St Edmunds; W M George MPS, Halesworth; Broomes Ltd, Woodford Green; Bevan & Stooke, Harwich; E W Judge, Bourne, Lincs; Coldwells Drug Store, Westcliff-on-Sea; W L Clifton, Westcliff-on-Sea; S Bruce Wilson MPS, Westcliff-on-Sea; G Peck & Son Ltd, Cambridge; Leonard W Stearn, Cambridge; Hutchinsons, Whittlesea, Cambs; J W Bodger, Peterborough; J Hillen MPS, Southend; T A Huxtable, Leigh-on-Sea.

A total of at least 108 pharmacies are represented in the collection.

CHRONOLOGY
Collection started in 1960.
Planning permission applied for building to house collection in 1974.
Planning permission granted in 1975.
Iceni Pharmacy built in summer 1976.
Accident with lorry in November 1976.
Pharmacy layout re-started Feb 1977.
Pharmacy opened in July 1977.
Permanent site for collection sought in 1982.
Transferred to Bridewell Museum in Oct 1984.
Collection opened to public in June 1985.
Cataloguing completed in 2002.

OLDEST ITEMS IN THE COLLECTION
Shelving from Smith & Son Norwich 1790.
Drug-runs from Row & Taylor Norwich 1854.

MOST RECENT ITEM
Baby scales from J Newstead, Sprowston 1960.

ABOUT THE AUTHOR

Norfolk-born John Newstead qualified as a pharmacist in 1955, moving back to Norwich in 1960 to open his first shop.

He was designated as a Fellow of The Royal Pharmaceutical Society of Great Britain in 1978 for his contribution to the history of pharmacy.

Now retired, he lives with his wife Janie in Taverham, Norfolk.

ACKNOWLEDGEMENTS
Thanks are due to John Renton, Curator of the Bridewell Museum, Norwich, Ron Bishop and his friends in the Fire Brigade for all their help and support, and Brian Lambert our sympathetic builder.